WINDERMERE:
RESTORING THE HEALTH OF ENGLAɴ

This book has been produced to celebrate the 50th Anniversary of the Lake District National Park and to inform readers about major issues of public interest concerning Windermere. Set in a deep glacial valley and surrounded by spectacular landscape, Windermere is the first lake encountered by thousands of tourists who come to the district each year. In summer the lake is teeming with pleasure craft of all shapes and sizes, whilst many other activities take place around its shores. In winter the lake is a quiet haven for numerous waterfowl and a few hardy people. The LDNP Authority and its Still Waters Partners are jointly responsible for overseeing and managing this national resource. They have to balance a wide variety of view-points and sometimes conflicting requirements against the natural 'needs' of Windermere itself, with the aim of maintaining the lake in an ecologically healthy state for public use and enjoyment now and in the future.

The account given here addresses major issues that scientific research on the lake has shown to be important for its flora and fauna. The author has been engaged in biological research on fresh waters for several decades and until recently was also Director of the Institute of Freshwater Ecology, now the Windermere Laboratory of the Centre for Ecology and Hydrology. With this background, Professor Pickering is well placed to provide a summary of past and present events that have dominated the historical development of Windermere since it was formed at the end of the last glaciation. In particular, his later chapters focus on the period in the second half of the 20th century when increased inputs of nutrients from treated sewage produced unwelcome growths of algae – a sure sign of declining health in the lake ecosystem. The development of large quantities of certain algae resulted in reduced oxygen concentrations that posed a serious threat to fish in the lake, especially the rare Arctic charr, a relict of the lake's glacial history.

The collaborative efforts of scientists and managers to restore the lake to a more healthy state, with thriving populations of fish and a suitably diverse fauna and flora, are described in non-technical language that is suitable for readers who do not have a scientific background. Where a few technical terms are necessary, these are explained in the text so that the principal processes occurring in this large and relatively deep lake can be readily understood. The author stresses that constant vigilance is required to identify warning signs of deterioration that are not always visible at the lake's surface.

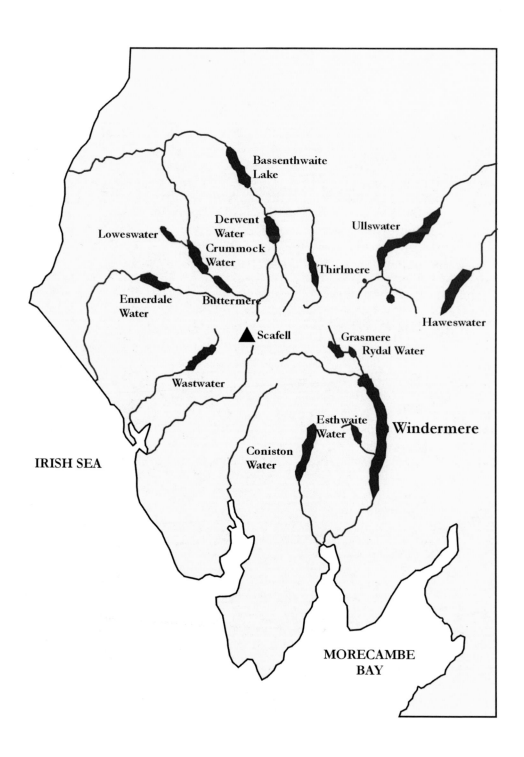

Bassenthwaite
Lake

Loweswater

Derwent
Water
Crummock
Water

Ullswater

Thirlmere

Ennerdale
Water

Buttermere

Haweswater

Scafell

Grasmere
Rydal Water

Wastwater

Esthwaite
Water

Windermere

IRISH SEA

Coniston
Water

MORECAMBE
BAY

FRONTISPIECE. *Above:* Oblique aerial photograph, looking northwards over Windermere North Basin. Bowness-on-Windermere is in the right foreground, with Belle Isle to the left. The distant hills mark the top (watershed) of the lake's catchment, including the Troutbeck fells (right) and Fairfield horseshoe (centre). The catchment of Windermere also includes High Raise, Langdale Pikes and Bowfell (off to the left of the picture), which drain into upper Langdale.

Left: Major lakes in the English Lake District, Cumbria.

Published on behalf of the Still Waters Partnership
English Lake District (Cumbria)

Windermere:

Restoring the health of England's largest lake

by A. D. Pickering

Former Director of the Centre for Ecology and Hydrology Windermere

EDITED by D. W. Sutcliffe

GRAPHICS DESIGN by Y. Dickens

FOREWORD by Barbara Young

Chief Executive, Environment Agency

Published by the Freshwater Biological Association
The Ferry House, Far Sawrey, Ambleside,
Cumbria LA22 0LP, UK

(Registered Charity No. 214440)

© Freshwater Biological Association, 2001

Special Publication No. 11
ISBN 0-900386-68-1; ISSN 0367-1887

Typeset in Book Antiqua and Times New Roman
by Drummond Typesetters Ltd

Printed by Titus Wilson & Son, Kendal, Cumbria

Contents

Foreword

Windermere is England's largest lake and arguably the most famous. Yet, despite its familiarity it is unlikely that many of us know much about events that have shaped the development and history of the lake, ranging from geological influences to human impacts over many centuries. The lake is much loved for its scenic beauty but is under continued pressures; indeed, it was in a critical condition just a few years ago. To allow this jewel in the crown of the English Lake District to deteriorate further would be unacceptable and we need to take all the measures necessary to protect this asset for future generations.

This will be no easy task. There is no single Authority, Agency, owner or user with sole responsibility. In view of the fact that the whole of the drainage catchment influences the lake's quality in numerous ways, the list of organisations and individuals with an interest in the lake becomes very large. Clearly, a partnership approach is paramount for all of us, not only as a means of resolving particular problems but also in establishing objectives for the lake that are designed to satisfy the needs and aspirations of most people.

We have been fortunate in having much high quality information on which decisions could be made. The Environment Agency encourages organisations that collect data to continue to maintain their efforts in order to ensure that future decisions can always be made on the basis of sound science. There needs to be excellent co-operation between organisations as they plan for the future. Ensuring the continued good quality of the lake is fundamental to the environment, the community and the local economy, all of which depend on it.

The first steps in the restoration of Windermere started well before the Lake District Still Waters Partnership was founded, but that group is now well placed to be a focus for resolving issues arising from land use, tourist pressures or any of the other potential challenges.

Windermere and its catchment do not stand alone, either geographically or ecologically. The lake is part of a living countryside, rich in wildlife, history and culture. It has been and continues to be the inspiration of poets, painters, writers and philosophers. The strategies that are now being formulated to protect Windermere and its neighbouring lakes and tarns play an integral part in the protection of the Lake District as a whole. The launch of the Lake District Still Waters Partnership, through the publication of this book, makes an important start to the aim of achieving World Heritage status for the English Lake District.

Environment Agency   Barbara Young
Rio House, Bristol   Chief Executive

Preface

In the 50th year of the Lake District National Park, it seemed most appropriate to draw the public's attention to the enormous amount of work that lies behind one of the Lake District's apparently natural assets. Even the most discerning visitor may be lulled into the false impression that Windermere is relatively unaffected by the activities of today's society. However, the lake increasingly has been influenced by mankind for nearly eight thousand years. So much so that during the lifetime of the National Park, and despite Windermere's relatively large volume (314 million cubic metres of water), water quality in the lake was severely threatened by enrichment with plant nutrients – a process that is sometimes referred to as "cultural eutrophication". A number of organisations had the scientific information, regulatory power and financial resources to limit this threat and even reverse it. This book, besides describing the origins of Windermere, gives an account of the threat, its limitation and reversal. The organisations have subsequently come together as the Lake District Still Waters Partnership so that they can act in a more co-ordinated and proactive way to promote and practice sound, scientifically-based, sustainable management for all of the waters in the Lake District. Their logos are shown at the beginning of the book and brief descriptions of what they do are included towards the end.

Remarkably, from the planning of the book to its publication, it has taken just over twelve months: this is in no small part due to the diligence of the author, Alan Pickering, with editorial support from David Sutcliffe and Graphics Design by Yvonne Dickens.

The reader, we hope, will be able to discern the value and magnitude of the scientific effort that has been devoted to the lake over the last seventy years. It is also satisfying to be able to recount an application of this knowledge which demonstrates a solution to a problem that we created. At the same time we can wonder at the beauty of the landscapes and their fauna and flora that are so well illustrated in the photographs.

Freshwater Biological Association   Roger Sweeting
The Ferry House, Ambleside   Chief Executive

Chapter 1
Introduction

"The clearness of the water (in Windermere) is a common surprise to the resident in a level country"

Miss Harriet Martineau's Guide to Windermere, 1854

"A first encounter with this lake could well confirm the impression that Windermere is a very well-used waterway"

W. Heaton Cooper, Lakeland Artist, 1966

The above quotations underline the aesthetic qualities of Windermere, England's largest natural lake, and its recreational amenity value. In addition, the lake is an important site for nature conservation, a source of drinking water and, indeed, a 'receiving' waterbody for treated waste effluents. With so many conflicting demands it is little wonder that concerns have been expressed about the long-term future of the health of the lake. This book is written for the interested non-specialist and describes the geological formation of the lake, the major aspects of human history in the Windermere catchment and inevitable human impacts on the water quality and ecology of the lake. It attempts to show how a 'partnership' approach to management has identified a growing water quality problem that threatened to destroy some of the unique fish populations in the lake. However, identifying a problem is one matter whereas finding a solution for it is quite another!

The North Basin of Windermere, viewed on a winter's afternoon, looking northwards from The Ferry House. Belle Isle is just to the right.

A relatively recent deterioration of water quality, in the form of reduced oxygen levels in the deeper parts of Windermere, has been linked to an increase in nutrients in the lake, in turn causing an excessive growth of microscopic plants (algae) in the water. Once the problem was recognised and quantified, a strategy for management was drawn up and evidence is presented to show that not only has this deterioration been halted, it has been reversed, to the benefit of fish in the lake. However, this is not a time for complacency, and constant vigilance is required if we are to maintain the progress made thus far and avoid similar problems in other parts of the English Lake District.

The North Basin of Windermere, looking west across to the distant massif of Bow Fell.

Lake management is a complex business involving a broad cross-section of the community and therefore interests inevitably conflict from time to time. This book identifies some of the main organisations with an involvement in Windermere but also makes the point that some of the most interested parties may well belong to following generations and their rights must also be protected. Partnership is a way of ensuring that expertise and knowledge is effectively shared, better use is made of combined resources, and management decisions are made with an improved understanding of the views of different organisations. It should involve those with a statutory role to conserve and protect the resource, those with a clear remit to make use of the water, and others who have a personal interest in the recreational attractions of the lake. A new partnership, the Lake District Still Waters Partnership, has been formed as a forum for both discussion and action, and this book, one of the first tangible outputs from the group, is published to commemorate the 50th Anniversary of the Lake District National Park. Further details of the new partnership are given in Chapter 9.

Four of the seven founder members of the Lake District Still Waters Partnership have been largely responsible for the work behind this demonstration project to restore the ecological health of Windermere. The Freshwater Biological Association and the Centre for Ecology and Hydrology (formerly the Institute of Freshwater Ecology) carried out the environmental research and interpretation (with financial support from the other two partners). The Environment Agency (formerly the National Rivers Authority) has played a key role as an environmental monitor and regulator. United Utilities (formerly North West Water) has been responsible for the practical implementation of technology to improve water quality in the lake. Working together, these four organisations have demonstrated the value of a partnership approach for solving complex environmental problems and an important message to come out of this project is that management decisions must be made on the basis of the best scientific information available at the time.

However, scientists tend to write for other scientists, often using a jargon that is incomprehensible to managers, planners, policy-makers and to the general public. The account given here is firmly based on the scientific literature but is written in a style intended to minimise the use of jargon. To do this has been a major challenge to the author and, although scientific terminology has been kept to a minimum, in some instances simple alternatives to scientific terms are not always available. In such cases, scientific terms are defined at their point of use within the text.

History of research on Windermere

It is understandable and appropriate that England's largest freshwater lake should be the focus of sustained, long-term scientific research. Indeed, work on the physics, chemistry and biology of Windermere has done much to develop limnology (the scientific study of lakes) on a worldwide basis. However, the beginnings of organised freshwater biology in Britain are to be found in the work of W. H. Pearsall, who started his studies of the English Lake District just before the First World War and developed the idea that the lakes formed a continuous series representing different stages in an evolutionary sequence. The lack of a national facility for biological research on fresh waters was underlined during the 1927 meeting of the British Association for the Advancement of Science, and in 1929

the Freshwater Biological Association of the British Empire was created, with W. H. Pearsall as its part-time director.

By 1931, suitable head-quarters had been found at Wray Castle, on the shores of Windermere, and a small group of scientists began research in earnest.

Wray Castle, a mock-Norman folly built in 1845 by a wealthy doctor from Liverpool. The castle is now owned by the National Trust.

At the start of the Second World War (1939) most of the seven scientific staff were called for war service, but evacuees arrived from the British Museum of Natural History and the Fisheries Laboratory at Lowestoft, and work on Windermere continued. Indeed, one project was specifically devoted to the war effort, when large numbers of perch were trapped and canned for human consumption (Chapter 5). In 1948 the Freshwater Biological Association (FBA) was awarded the Eimar Naumann Medal at the International Limnological Congress, confirming the growing international scientific reputation of the laboratory. Facilities at Wray Castle were beginning to prove inadequate and in 1950 the laboratory and forty-one staff were transferred to the Ferry Hotel, some four miles down the lake on its western shore. As The Ferry House, it still is the headquarters of the Association. Growth continued and in 1965 the River Laboratory was established on the River Frome in Dorset. Space at The Ferry House was also becoming restrictive so, in 1973 an adjoining, newly constructed Pearsall Building was opened.

Aerial view of The Ferry House on the western shore of Windermere, headquarters of the FBA since 1950 and shared with IFE (1989-1994) and CEH Windermere (since 1994). The relatively new Pearsall Building is on the left; a queue of vehicles waiting for the ferry can be seen on the right.

Until the 1970s the research of the Association was primarily of a fundamental nature, as progress was made to understand some of the key processes controlling freshwater ecosystems. However, there was now a growing feeling in government circles that science should be more orientated towards solving practical

Motor launch *Velia*. Specially-built for use in scientific research, the 30-ft launch has a shallow draught, is very stable in the water and capable of operating in all weather conditions. It has been in service for the FBA, IFE and CEH Windermere since 1958. The launch is aptly named after the water-cricket *Velia saulii*, a small waterbug that lives on the surface at the edges of sheltered bays in the lake and frequents the bay behind The Ferry House, where the launch is moored. *Velia* is regularly used for obtaining water samples, algae and other planktonic organisms which are sampled at fixed buoys in the North and South Basins of Windermere. *Velia* is also used for sampling fish, and is fitted with echo-location equipment.

problems, and major changes were made to the mechanisms for funding scientific research. The aim was to ensure that the science was of direct value to the 'end-user' and this produced a shift in emphasis of the research programme towards more applied work under specific contract to customers such as government departments, conservation organisations, managers and the water industry. Clearly it was also important to continue a core element of fundamental research in order to understand the potential environmental problems of the future. The subject of this book, the restoration of the ecological health of Windermere, is an excellent example of the application of basic research to the solution of a real environmental problem.

Further major changes were to follow. In 1989 the Natural Environment Research Council (NERC, the major funding organisation behind the FBA) undertook the management of the large majority of the Association's staff and all the facilities to create the Institute of Freshwater Ecology (IFE). The Institute continued to develop the strategic and applied research programme and worked closely with 'customer' departments (including some members of the Lake District Still Waters Partnership). The FBA, now much reduced in size, changed the emphasis of its scientific role to focus on serving the needs of its international membership of some two thousand professional and amateur environmental scientists and naturalists, and to running a smaller programme of more fundamental research, designed to complement (but not compete with) the Institute's research programme.

Individual membership of the FBA is open to anyone interested in freshwater science and who wishes to share the Association's resources, information and expertise (contact details are given at the back of this book). In 1994, the NERC created a new umbrella structure, the Centre for Ecology and Hydrology (CEH), for its environmental research institutes, in a move to promote interdisciplinary research teams capable of tackling some of the larger environmental problems facing the planet. The Centre for Ecology and Hydrology included the Institute of Freshwater Ecology, the Institute of Terrestrial Ecology, the Institute of Hydrology and the Institute of Virology and Environmental Microbiology. Further integration occurred in 1999 when the institute structure was abandoned and CEH became a single organisation, of which the Windermere Laboratory is an important component.

The source material for this book is largely derived from the extensive joint library holdings of the Freshwater Biological Association and CEH Windermere, much of it as original published research papers. However, significant input has also been made by the member organisations of the Lake District Still Waters Partnership and, therefore, this book has drawn upon a wealth of information and expertise in different areas (see the acknowledgements for the long list of contributors). Some of the more accessible and readable literature, and key contact addresses and websites, are listed at the end of the book for those who might wish to pursue particular issues in more detail. The overall message of the book is that the application of good science, within a partnership framework of environmental managers and 'end-users', can be used to create sustainable solutions to complex environmental problems.

Chapter 2
How the Lake District was formed

In order to appreciate and understand England's largest lake, we first need to go back in time to discover some of the enormous natural forces responsible for its creation. Most people are aware that the lakes of the English Lake District are 'glacial' in origin but where did the landmass, on which the ice sheets of the last glaciation carved their signature, come from? To understand this requires a journey back in time over hundreds of millions of years. The geological structure of the Lake District is complex, because the wide range of rock-types represents much of the world's geological timescale. A simplified map (page 8) and diagram (page 9) show the major rock-types that form the present-day landscape of the region.

If we retrace the geological history of the area back to its oldest rocks, we can see how this complex pattern of rocks developed. Even today, the underlying geology has important effects on the physico-chemical and biological characteristics of the lakes in the area, including the lakes of the Windermere catchment.

The geology of the Lake District

Regular visitors to the Lake District will always notice change. This might be seen as variable weather patterns, seasonal changes in the vegetation or, perhaps, new property developments. However, to most of us who enjoy the area, the hills and lakes are signs of permanence in a changing world. This perception is misleading because the definition of 'permanent' largely depends upon the timescale used. Certainly, over a human lifetime the fells of the Lake District are more or less constant features but, when considered over geological time, there is clear evidence of massive and continuous change. The world's crust is in a state of constant flux, as new landmasses appear, others disappear and some move to different parts of the planet's surface.

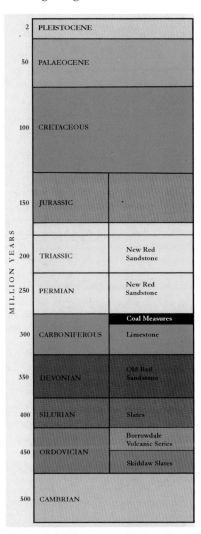

Simplified diagram of geological time relevant to rock-types in the English Lake District.

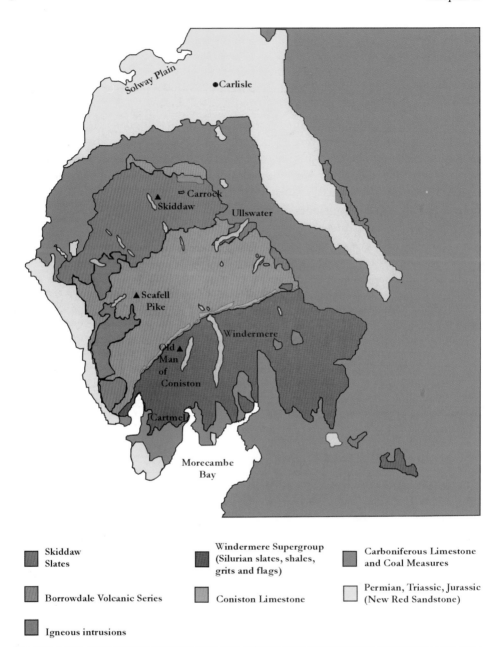

Skiddaw Slates

Borrowdale Volcanic Series

Windermere Supergroup (Silurian slates, shales, grits and flags)

Coniston Limestone

Carboniferous Limestone and Coal Measures

Permian, Triassic, Jurassic (New Red Sandstone)

Igneous intrusions

Simplified map of major rock-types in the English Lake District. The central fells and crags are formed by volcanic rocks of the Ordovician Period. More rounded fells to the north consist of earlier Ordovician sedimentary Skiddaw Slates. The lower fells in the south of the Lake District are formed from sedimentary rocks laid down in the Silurian period. Formerly known as the Bannisdale or Silurian Slates, they are now called the Windermere Supergroup of sedimentary rocks. Surrounding the Lakeland fells, low-lying and coastal areas lie on Carboniferous limestone, including seams of coal, and on the remnants of later sedimentary rocks formed in Permian, Triassic and Jurassic periods.

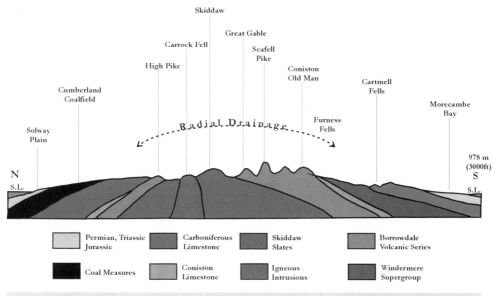

Simplified cross-section of major geological features from north to south across the Lake District.

Large-scale movements of the earth's crust are not normally obvious to the untrained eye, but reports of volcanic eruptions and earthquakes from many different parts of the world are constant reminders of the fluidity of the thin 'solid' crust overlying the vast bulk of the planet. With this in mind, we will now retrace the geological history of the Cumbrian landmass to see how it explains what we now see as the landscape of the Lake District.

The English Lake District consists of a mass of ancient rocks, in three major bands running east-north-east to west-south-west, surrounded by a rim of appreciably newer rocks. The oldest are the Skiddaw Slates (Skiddaw Group) in the north of the area. These sedimentary rocks consist of a series of darkish-coloured slates with occasional coarser grits, laid down some five hundred to four hundred and fifty million years ago (in the early Ordovician Period, when the region was covered by a shallow sea). Some of the fossils in these rocks confirm their marine, sedimentary origin and include graptolites – extinct forms of colonial, marine invertebrates.

To the south of these oldest rocks we find a broad band of hard rocks with a very different origin. This is the Borrowdale Volcanic Series, the name of which gives away both its origin and its location. The Borrowdale Volcanic Series were formed in the late Ordovician, some four hundred and fifty to four hundred and ten million years ago, during a period of enormous volcanic activity, with lava flows and huge eruptions of gas and dust. Eventually the volcanic activity subsided, leaving behind a mixture of solidified lava, ashes and dust that became the rocks we see today. Given their violent geological history, it ought not to surprise us that these rocks are devoid of fossils. However, they do provide much of the mineral wealth in the area (Chapter 5). Some of the volcanic rocks in this series have significantly more resistance to erosion, leaving behind a landscape with a much more rugged silhouette than that of the sedimentary slates to the north; the hardest give rise to well-defined slabs, buttresses and ridges. Scafell Pike, the highest point in the Lake District (978 metres above sea-level), is composed of such volcanic rocks. Being relatively resistant to erosion, the Borrowdale Volcanic rocks do not have a large 'buffering' capacity with which to counteract the effects of acid rain (Chapter 5). It is understandable, therefore, that some of the most acid waters in the region are to be found in the central Lake District, overlying these relatively unreactive rocks. The Borrowdale Volcanic Series also include some layers of slate, representing mud-flows and very fine ashes which were subsequently affected by pressure and heat. Some of these, such as the green slates of Honister and Elterwater, make superior roofing slates and building material compared with the Skiddaw Slates.

At the south-eastern limit of the Borrowdale Volcanic Series of rocks there is a very narrow band of Coniston Limestone. The cause of much speculation and scientific discussion, this series is much older than the Carboniferous limestone surrounding much of the Lake District and was formed in the late Ordovician Period at a time when the area was inundated by warm, shallow seas. Outcrops of these rocks can be seen north-west of Coniston, on either side of the North Basin of Windermere, and to the north of Kentmere. Look out for small, historical lime-kilns associated with the narrow band of rock – lime was used in the area for 'white-washing' buildings and for 'sweetening' the thin soils.

The southern part of the Lake District is composed of sedimentary rocks laid down in the Silurian Period (approximately 400 million years ago) at a time when the landmass was located to the south of the equator, at the margins of a continent. Covered by a warm, shallow ocean teeming with life, sediments of sand and mud accumulated to a depth of over five kilometres and eventually formed the rocks now called the Windermere Supergroup of shales, slates, grits and flags (formerly known as the Bannisdale Slates). Fossil evidence reveals a marine life consisting of crinoids, trilobites, brachiopods and corals. The countryside in this area is much less rugged than that to the north, with few hills over one thousand feet in height (300 metres).

Moving forward in geological time, the Lake District was successively covered by Devonian rocks and then by limestone from the Carboniferous Period (340 to 280 million years ago), when the area was located just to the north of the equator and was covered by a shallow, tropical sea. Abundant marine life is evident from the fossil corals and shellfish. During the Permian-Triassic Period (280 to 195 million years ago) the land was uplifted and became increasingly arid. This period of desertification was followed by the Jurassic Period (the 'age of the dinosaurs', some 195 to 140 million years ago) when water once again brought its life-giving forces and the seas were dominated by plesiosaurs, ichthyosaurs and sea-crocodiles. Much of this geological history has disappeared from the Lake District as the overlying younger rocks have been lost through land uplift, creating the 'Cumbrian Dome' which was then eroded over time, removing the younger rock formations. However, the surrounding parts of Cumbria bear witness to these more recent geological periods. Carboniferous limestone cliffs can be seen near Kendal and Grange-over–Sands and, until our more recent sensitivity to environmental issues, 'waterworn Westmorland limestone' had been a popular choice of gardeners for rockery construction. Its use as a decorative feature along wall tops and in buildings was also very common. Carboniferous coal deposits in north-west Cumbria were the primary reason for industrial development in the Whitehaven/Workington area over the past two centuries and the Permian-Triassic history can be seen in the 'New Red Sandstones' of St Bees, the Solway Plain and the Eden valley.

Early Palaeozoic rocks are believed to underlie the whole region and the existing surface geology is complicated by diverse and ore-rich mineral deposits which have had a marked influence on human mining activities in the area (Chapter 5). Complex folding, uplifting of the earth's crust and granitic intrusions from deeper layers have contorted the stratigraphy of the rocks (the sequential record of rock formation), although the basic features of the geological map can be easily recognised from a simplified geological cross-section of Cumbria (p. 9). This underlying geology has been the raw material on which the intermittent forces of ice sheets have worked during the last two million years or so. Indeed, the existing landscape is primarily the product of a period of ice cover (the Devensian) that reached its peak some twenty-two thousand years ago.

The influence of the Ice Age on lake formation

The 'Ice Age' is used as a popular term for part of the most recent geological period of time, the Pleistocene, which takes us forward to the present day. The Lake District has been covered by ice several times during the last two million years. Four main periods of total ice cover are normally recognised, the second of which was the most extensive. During this glacial period, the ice sheet extended as far south as a line somewhere between the Bristol Channel and the River Thames. However the last period of ice cover largely obliterated the evidence of earlier glacial episodes in the Lake District and is primarily responsible for many of the landscape features that we see today. Between these periods of complete ice cover, the climate became warmer, possibly even warmer than the present day, and these ice-free times are known as 'interglacial' or 'interstadial' periods, depending on their duration. It is not unreasonable to believe that our present climate represents an interglacial period, ultimately to be followed by another glaciation. When considered in terms of the geological timescale, the topical issue of global warming due to atmospheric pollution may have a small but temporary impact on this process.

The last ice sheet covering the Lake District formed a huge dome up to one kilometre thick. Never static, this mass of ice expanded and contracted in a predominantly radial fashion, scouring out the lines of least resistance. These activities resulted in the displacement and destruction of millions of tons of rock as the typical features of a glacial landscape were created. It is, perhaps, a little too simplistic to represent the movements of the ice sheet as radial because, at the edges, it came into contact with other 'tongues' of ice moving in different directions. Thus a major influence in the north was a southerly movement of ice from the Southern Uplands of Scotland, and boulders of granite from the northern shores of the Solway Firth have been left stranded as far inland as the shores of Bassenthwaite Lake! Such displaced boulders are referred to as 'erratics'. Other ice moved south-eastwards along the Vale of Eden. Interactions between ice sheets moving in somewhat different directions can also be found in the west and south of the county where the 'Cumbrian' ice sheet met the Irish ice sheet.

The most active components of the ice sheets covering Cumbria were the glaciers that advanced and retreated up and down the existing valleys. The sheer power of slow-moving masses of ice was sufficient to straighten valleys, turning them into wider and deeper dales, as in Langdale, and leaving behind a

variety of other landscape features that give the Lake District its characteristic appearance. It must be recognised that what we see today is not just the product of one glaciation but is the combined result of successive periods of ice cover. Typical glacial features are the large protrusions of bedrock that are rounded, polished or scoured on the 'up-stream' surface of the rock in this flow of ice, but

Mickleden in upper Langdale, a typical valley eroded by ice.

rough and broken on the 'downstream' side. These are the 'roches moutoneés', so named by De Saussure because their form resembles the wavy wigs styled 'moutoneés' during the 18th century (the wigs were actually greased with mutton fat to keep their shiny appearance!). During the valley-straightening process, the glaciers tended to plane off any projections to form 'truncated spurs'. Some smaller side-tributary valleys have been left 'hanging' through glacial deepening of the main valleys, resulting in the formation of spectacular waterfalls, such as Dungeon Ghyll, as the streams plummet into the main valley. Small rounded hills or 'drumlins' are also typical glacial landscape features; good examples of these may be found in the region between Kendal and Lancaster.

The Lake District would not be so interesting or spectacular without its high altitude tarns, many of which lie in typical, circular rock-basins. The mechanisms of corrie formation have been the subject of much scientific debate but are believed to include alternate freezing and thawing of the basin walls, ultimately shattering the rock, and rotational abrasion by the corrie glacier. Good examples are Scales Tarn on Blencathra

A landscape of grass-covered hummocks, the remains of glacial debris dumped on Dunmail Rise by retreating ice.

(Skiddaw), Red Tarn on Helvellyn, and Blea Water under the eastern face of High Street. One of the early expeditions of the Brathay Exploration Group from Brathay Hall (a former villa on the shores of Windermere and now home of the Brathay Hall Trust) first reported (in 1948) the spectacular sixty-three metres depth of Blea Water, a discovery that helped to develop theories of corrie formation. In some areas, such as Dunmail Raise, the head of Langdale and the outer edge of Easedale corrie, material deposited by the retreating glaciers has resulted in a characteristic hummocky landscape.

Of course, some of the most obvious and impressive features of the Lake District's recent glacial history are the lakes themselves. Almost all of the large glaciated valleys in the area are occupied by lakes. These were created when the glaciers finally retreated, often leaving behind a pile of debris, a 'terminal moraine', at the lower end of the valley and forming a natural barrier or dam. The final glacial retreat from Cumbria occurred in stages between seventeen and ten thousand years ago. Pioneer vegetation occurred in the Windermere catchment some thirteen thousand years ago but this was followed by a further cold period and reversal to tundra conditions. However, by twelve to ten thousand years before present times the ice had left behind a network of large lakes, more or less similar in form to that seen today, draining in a radial pattern from the central dome of volcanic rock towards the periphery of the Lake District.

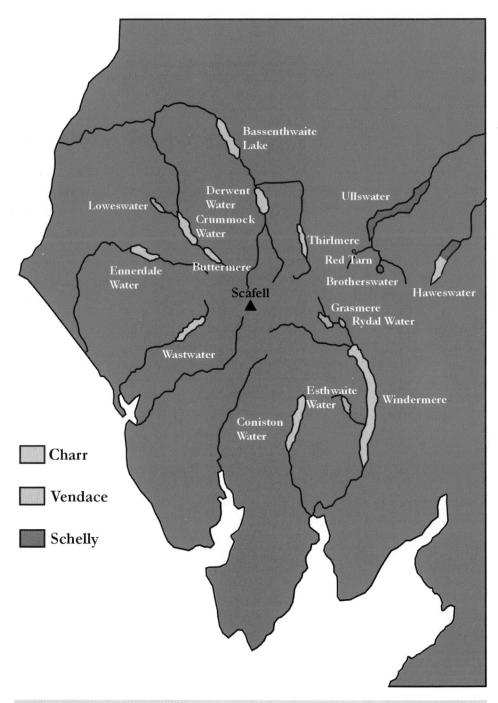

Radial distribution of river valleys around Scafell Pike, the highest peak in the Lake District at 978 metres. Lakes containing rare fish are also shown, including Brotherswater and Red Tarn in the catchment of Ullswater.

Windermere is distinctive by being the largest of the lakes but it also has many features in common with other lakes of the area. In general, they are deep, narrow, ribbon-shaped waterbodies oriented rather like the spokes of a wheel. Several of the lakes contain cold-water species of fish (glacial relicts) that, on a national scale, are considered to be rare. The Arctic charr *Salvelinus alpinus* can be found in Buttermere, Coniston Water, Crummock Water, Ennerdale Water, Haweswater, Thirlmere, Wastwater and Windermere. An even rarer fish, the schelly *Coregonus lavaretus*, occurs in a group of four lakes in the eastern part of the Lake District, namely Haweswater, Brotherswater, Red Tarn and Ullswater, and the rarest fish of all, the vendace *Coregonus albula*, only occurs in the two most northerly lakes, Bassenthwaite Lake and Derwent Water. These are the only populations of vendace now remaining in the whole of the UK. The conservation of these glacial relict fish species is of growing importance because three of the populations, the charr in Windermere, the schelly in Haweswater and the vendace in Bassenthwaite Lake, have shown recent signs of decline. The Windermere charr populations are considered in more detail in Chapter 4, and Chapter 7 describes how this species is now recovering, following improvements in water quality within the lake.

Having emphasised some of the similarities between the lakes, it is important to recognise that there are also differences in shape and form that can influence the way in which the different lakes respond to climatic signals or to some of the influences of human activities. Although Windermere is the largest of the lakes, it is not the deepest. That distinction goes to Wastwater, with a maximum water depth of seventy-six metres (some 250 feet). Interestingly, because the surface of Wastwater is only sixty-one metres (200 feet) above sea level, the bed of the lake is actually below sea level (a similar situation applies to Windermere). In comparison, lakes such as Bassenthwaite Lake and Derwent Water are relatively shallow in relation to their surface areas. This physical characteristic is important because shallow lakes are much more susceptible to mixing and turbulence caused by winds blowing across the surface. Moreover, from the previous section in this Chapter, we now understand a little more about the underlying geology of each lake catchment and this, in turn, influences the water chemistry of the different lakes.

The life history of a lake

Having argued previously that continents and oceans are only temporary features over geological time, it ought not to come as a surprise to know that freshwater lakes are constantly changing and that they also have a finite lifespan. Lakes may be formed by a variety of mechanisms, of which glacial activity is only one. The large African lakes have been created as the result of fault lines and subsequent movement in the earth's crust. Rising water-tables can create new lakes in low-lying hollows, and the erosional/depositional activities of lowland rivers may form ox-bow lakes. Volcanic eruptions can, eventually, lead to the development of crater lakes. Whatever its origin, any lake will be subjected to forces which ultimately may result in its disappearance. This is particularly important in the case of man-made lakes, such as water-storage reservoirs, where life expectancy of the waterbody is relatively short.

Lakes are not simply holes in the ground filled with water. The water itself may have a physical structure (Chapter 3 gives a description of thermal stratification in lakes) and the lake ecosystem is subject to the forces of nature, be they physical, chemical or biological. Some of these forces, as we have already seen, may generate lake basins, but others promote a natural progression from an open waterbody, through a process of successive colonisation, to wetland and, eventually, to dry land. The rate at which this succession is achieved varies enormously, from a matter of a few decades or centuries in the case of small waterbodies to millions of years. The world's largest lake, Lake Baikal in Siberia, is over twenty million years old and is still, very definitely, an open body of water! Evidence of change over the last fifteen to ten thousand years in the major lakes of the English Lake District is abundantly clear and, therefore, when tracing the history of Windermere as an open body of water we cannot expect things to remain static.

Although ice was the principal architect in the creation of the Cumbrian lakes, much of their subsequent change has resulted from the activity of running water.

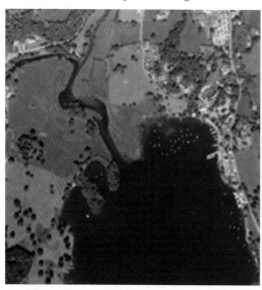

Aerial view of the head of Windermere, showing the delta of the River Brathay (top left in the picture).

The underlying rocks of the Lake District are still eroding, but at differing rates depending upon their geological composition. This means that even today, the streams deliver a fluctuating load of rocks, pebbles, gravel, silts and mud to the lakes. Of course, once this material reaches a lake, the physical force of the water-flow decreases and the solid materials are deposited on the bed of the lake, which acts as an enormous sediment trap. This is not a random process, however; the coarser material is deposited near the mouths of inflowing rivers and the finer, suspended matter travels further out into the lake before finally settling. By this process, river deltas build up at the head of a lake. The River Brathay, at the head of Windermere, has a very clear delta. This type of activity can be so intense that it completely changes the original shape of a lake.

A good example is Derwent Water, where the delta of the River Derwent is slowly pushing out into the southern end of the lake and has already filled in the head of the lake in Borrowdale. In some valleys this infilling process has resulted in the complete disappearance of former lakes. The Kentmere valley originally contained a series of lakes, the upper ones becoming filled with alluvium (sand, silt and mud brought down by rivers). In contrast, the lower lake was filled with the remains of aquatic plants, including large numbers of diatoms (microscopic algae), forming diatomaceous earth or diatomite. This material, when the organic matter is removed, is nothing more than the silica remains of ancient organisms that flourished in the lake when it was an open body of water. The diatomite has been extracted (thereby recreating the lake environment) and exploited by humans as a valuable insulation material and for mopping up oil-spills.

The example of lower Kentmere is an extreme case of a lake disappearing largely as a result of its own biological activity. Plant life in lakes can be divided into two basic types, the large marginal plants and 'water weeds' with which most of us are familiar, and smaller (usually microscopic) plants that often float freely in the water, the algae, of which diatoms are just one type. When algae die, their remains slowly sink to the bed of the lake and add to the accumulating layers of mineral and organic mud, slowly reducing the depth of the lake. Lake Baikal (mentioned earlier in this Chapter) has a maximum water depth of more than a mile (1.6 kilometres) but beneath that, mud has accumulated to a depth of more than four miles (7 kilometres). Needless to say this accumulation has occurred during twenty million years.

Aquatic plants, like their terrestrial counterparts, need a mixture of minerals and nutrients to enable them to grow. Originally, the chemistry of lake-waters was largely determined by rapid weathering of the glacial debris (ranging from finely ground rock-flour to roughened boulders and scoured rock-faces) in the catchment, and the water would have been slightly alkaline. Subsequently, much of the readily available minerals were also leached from the soils, and organic matter accumulated from the developing plant communities. This process ultimately decreased the availability of mineral nutrients to the lakes and increased the acidity of the water. Windermere has been going through such a cycle but, because of more recent inputs of plant nutrients resulting from human activities within the catchment, this slow natural cycle has been reversed (Chapter 6).

The sedimentary record in Windermere

The constant sedimentation of algal remains and other materials, from the lake and its catchment, not only contributes to the infilling process but also provides an historical record of the changes that have occurred over time. The most recently deposited material on the bed of a lake is at the sediment/water interface, with older material buried beneath it. Up to six metres of mud have accumulated on top of the original glacial gravel, silts and clays in Windermere, during the last ten thousand years. Information from the glacial debris has enabled us to

A Mackereth pneumatic core-sampler rises dramatically to the surface. Using compressed air, a long plastic pipe is driven down into relatively soft sediments to obtain an undisturbed core four to five centimetres in diameter and up to six metres in length. The large drum at the bottom of the sampler provides stability by holding the corer against the top of the sediment. After returning to the surface of the lake the corer is taken to the shore. Water pressure is then used to force a piston through the pipe, gently pushing the core out (rather like squeezing tooth-paste from its tube) and into narrow troughs; these hold the sediments in their current sequence of layers deposited since the late post-glacial. Subsequently, thin sections are taken for chemical and biological analysis in the laboratory.

The portable core-sampler was invented by John Mackereth. Born in Ambleside, he was analytical chemist at the FBA from 1946 to 1972. He invented and developed several other devices and methods for analysing very small amounts of substances present in water and sediments, including an ion-exchange system for measuring concentrations of solutes in Lake District waters, and an oxygen electrode (galvanic cell) for measuring oxygen concentrations.

trace the progression of the last glaciation and helped us to understand some of its impacts on the landscape. The overlying organic mud is packed with physical, chemical and biological clues, tracing the history of the lake and its valley since the last ice sheet retreated. Intact sediment cores can be extracted from the bed of the lake using special sampling tools operated by compressed air and, in the laboratory, these cores can be analysed in detail. Preserved pollen grains tell us about the local vegetation, remains of algae indicate the conditions within the lake, and recent bands of pollutants are a reminder of global events such as testing nuclear weapons in the atmosphere during the 1960s and the Chernobyl nuclear-reactor disaster in 1986. Most of the human impacts on Windermere, outlined in Chapter 5, have left their mark on the sediments of the lake, and the historical sequence can be reconstructed. Moreover, the timing of events can be ascertained from radioisotope and/or magnetic dating of the sediment cores.

Chapter 3
The lake and its catchment

Lakes are not isolated entities and it is important to consider not only the water-body but also its catchment, the area from which rainfall flows (via streams and rivers) into the lake. It is the most natural unit on which to base management plans, because any activity within the catchment has the potential to cause changes within the lake. The Windermere catchment is relatively large (230.5 square kilometres) and contains several other significant still waters. To the north of Windermere lie Grasmere and Rydal Water, with Loughrigg Tarn and Elterwater to the north-west. Blelham Tarn and Esthwaite Water are located to the west and several other smaller tarns occur within the Windermere catchment. The main inflows to Windermere are the Rivers Brathay and Rothay, at the head of the lake, Trout Beck, draining the north-east side of the catchment, and Cunsey Beck which drains the Esthwaite Water sub-catchment. The outflow from Windermere is the River Leven, which discharges into Morecambe Bay via an estuary shared with the River Crake, the outflow from Coniston Water.

The southern part of the Windermere catchment lies on Silurian shales of the Windermere Supergroup, whereas the northern part lies on rocks of the Borrowdale Volcanic Series (Chapter 2). These two contrasting parts of the catchment are separated by a thin band of Coniston Limestone. The lower slopes of the catchment are covered by glacial deposits of various thicknesses, with alluvial deposits on the valley floors of the Rivers Rothay and Brathay. In general the soils are poor but have been 'improved' by modern agricultural activity (Chapter 5). The climate of the Windermere catchment is oceanic, with mild winters and, considering the latitude (54° N), there is a small, seasonal temperature range. Predominantly westerly winds ensure that the average rainfall in the catchment is high, at over two metres per year. However, this mean figure disguises an almost three-fold difference in rainfall which decreases markedly from the head of the Langdale valley (3.8 metres per year) to the estuary of the River Leven (1.3 metres per year).

Windermere – the lake

Windermere is the most southerly of the major lakes in the English Lake District and, like many of the larger Cumbrian waterbodies, it is narrow and ribbon-shaped. The lake takes its name from the Norse but the precise origin is still the subject of debate. According to W. Heaton Cooper, the famous Lakeland artist, Windermere means the lake of Vinund (a personal name that occurs in the Old Norse language of Iceland). Other sources suggest that it is Vinandr's lake or Vinand's lake, also derived from Old Norse personal names to which the Old English term 'mere' was later added.

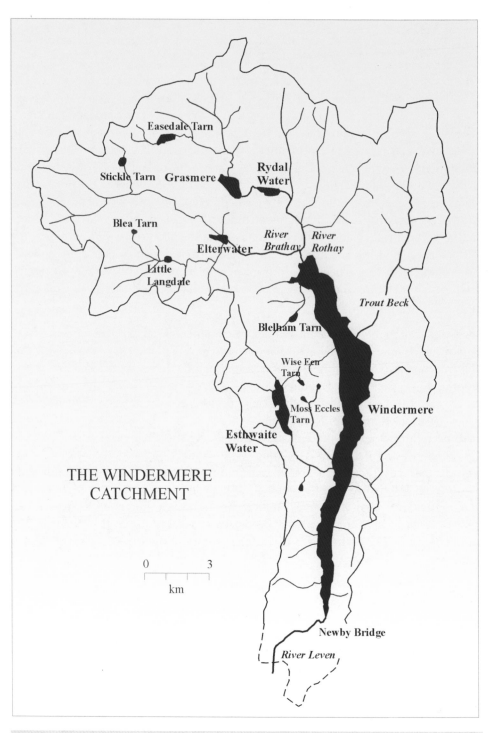

Easedale Tarn

Rydal
Water

Stickle Tarn   Grasmere

Blea Tarn

Elterwater   *River
Brathay*   *River
Rothay*

Little
Langdale

Trout Beck

Blelham Tarn

Wise Een
Tarn

Moss Eccles
Tarn   **Windermere**

Esthwaite
Water

THE WINDERMERE
CATCHMENT

0   3
⊢   ⊢   ⊣
km

Newby Bridge

River Leven

Lakes, tarns and major streams in the catchment of Windermere.

Oblique aerial photograph, looking south over Esthwaite Water, with Windermere South Basin in the distance at top left of the picture. The small tarn nearest the camera is Priest Pot, in which the microbiological flora and fauna has been studied intensively for many years. Esthwaite North Fen (a National Nature Reserve) is the area covered by small trees and shrubs immediately between Priest Pot and the head of Esthwaite Water beyond the tarn. The B5285 road from Sawrey and the Windermere ferry runs alongside the eastern side of the lake, turning west to enter Hawkshead village (just off the picture at bottom right). The gently undulating landscape of the southern catchment of Windermere lies on sedimentary rocks of the Windermere Supergroup; it is largely covered by woodland in the south but consists of agricultural pasture-land north of Esthwaite Water. The latter is an important source of water flowing into Windermere South Basin, via Cunsey Beck, making a noticeable difference to the chemistry of water in the South Basin.

Above: Elterwater, formed where the River Brathay and Great Langdale Beck meet. *Below:* Grasmere, in the valley of the River Rothay, looking down the lake to Rydal Water beyond. These small lakes lie on the Borrowdale Volcanic Series of rocks in the catchment of Windermere North Basin.

Above: Little Langdale Tarn, near Elterwater, in the catchment of Windermere North Basin, looking west. *Below:* Blelham Tarn, looking north-east towards Wansfell Pike and Loughrigg Fell; Ambleside lies between these fells. Windermere North Basin is just visible at centre right of the picture; Blelham Tarn lies in its catchment but is on rocks of the Windermere Supergroup.

The origin of Windermere's name may be uncertain but it is tautology to make the common mistake of calling it 'Lake Windermere'. Indeed, many of us will have fallen for the trick question: "How many lakes are there in the English Lake District?". The answer is one, Bassenthwaite Lake, because all the others are either *meres* (Buttermere, Thirlmere, Windermere, etc.) or *waters* (Coniston Water, Brothers Water, Ennerdale Water, Esthwaite Water, etc.).

Some seventeen kilometres long and about one kilometre wide, Windermere is England's largest natural lake, containing over three hundred and fourteen million cubic metres (69 thousand million gallons) of water. On the UK scale, Windermere is overshadowed by Loch Ness, which is approximately twice as long, twice as wide and four times deeper than Windermere. In fact there is more fresh water in Loch Ness than in all of the Cumbrian lakes put together. Extending the comparison even further, Lake Baikal in Siberia contains three thousand times more water than Loch Ness and accounts for twenty percent of (unfrozen) fresh water in the world. Thus, on an international scale Windermere is a mere puddle – but an important puddle, nevertheless!

Windermere is almost two lakes, consisting of a North Basin (maximum depth 64 metres) and a South Basin (maximum depth 42 metres). These two deep basins are separated by an area of relative shallows (average depth 10 metres) in the centre of the lake, where most of the islands are to be found.

An aerial view of Windermere, looking north towards the fells above the valley of Trout Beck (top centre right). Belle Isle is in the centre of the picture, with Bowness-on-Windermere to the right and Claife Heights to the left. The Ferry House is on the small peninsula just below Belle Isle, where the Windermere Ferry crosses the lake.

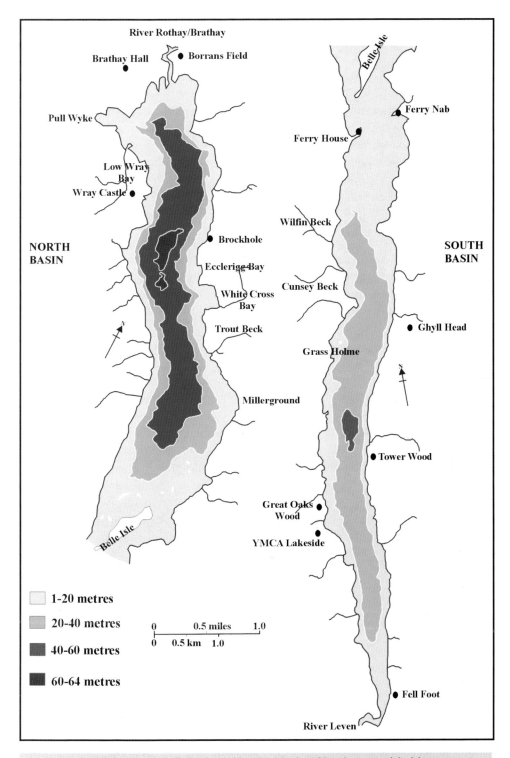

Bathymetric map of Windermere, with major islands and locations around the lake.

The lake also becomes slightly narrower at this point, where the Bowness to Hawkshead car ferry service runs (Chapter 5). In many respects the two basins of the lake function as two separate lakes, with significant differences in water chemistry (see below), fish populations (Chapter 4) and water quality (Chapter 6). More than four hundred million cubic metres of water flow through the lake each year and the retention time (the average length of time for a drop of water entering the lake to leave it down the River Leven) is approximately nine months. The terminal moraine blocking the southern exit to the Windermere valley currently retains the present lake but its water-level is now controlled at 39.1 metres (128.4 feet) above sea-level by a weir at Newby Bridge, constructed in 1971. Thus the deepest parts of both basins are actually below sea-level. At high water-flows the bridge is also a constraint to the passage of water, and lake-levels may be elevated by more than one metre during very rainy spells.

The depth of both North and South Basins is sufficient to ensure that both parts of the lake undergo an annual process called *thermal stratification*. In the spring, as the sun's power becomes greater, the lake begins to warm up. However, because the heat input is to the surface water, only this is heated. Warm water is less dense than cold water and so it tends to stay at the surface (an electric kettle works quite differently; heat input is at the bottom and warm water then rises to mix the whole kettle). By early summer the lake becomes thermally stratified and consists of an upper warmer layer of water floating on top of a deeper colder layer, with relatively little mixing between the two layers. The transition between the warm and cold parts of the lake is called the *thermocline* which, in Windermere during summer, is normally located some five to ten metres below the surface of the lake. Indeed, the depth of the thermocline from the surface is an approximate indication of the weather conditions during the spring and summer. In a good summer (i.e. one with frequent sunshine!) the thermocline will be nearer the surface of the lake, whereas in a poor summer (cloudy and wet) the thermocline will be deeper. Moreover, recent research has also shown that the depth of the thermocline is linked, in quite subtle ways, to the behaviour of the Gulf Stream in the North Atlantic (Chapter 9). As autumn progresses and the lake cools down, heat is lost from the surface of the lake. Eventually (usually in late October/early November in the South Basin and a little later in the North Basin), autumn gales have sufficient energy to re-mix the entire lake and the temperature again becomes similar at all depths during the winter months. The whole cycle is then repeated in the following year.

The process of thermal stratification has a marked influence on the chemistry and biology of the lake during the summer months and is one of the main reasons for the survival of glacial relict fish populations (Chapter 4). Thus, during the warm summer of 1976, surface temperatures in the lake reached 24°C but the deepest water was still less than 8°C. This ensured that there was ample cool water for Arctic charr to survive in the lake.

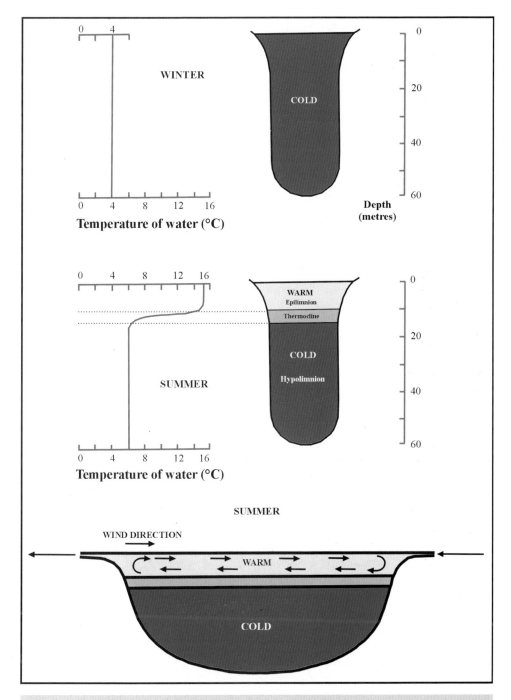

Diagrams illustrating winter and summer temperatures in Windermere. Deep water remains cool throughout the year, providing a refuge for cold-water fish such as Arctic charr, where the water is well oxygenated. The fish prefer cold water as it naturally holds more oxygen than warm water (30% more at 5°C than at 25°C).

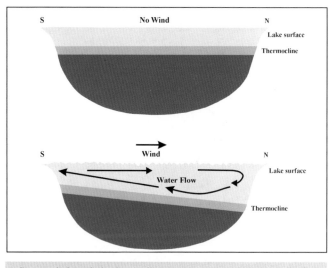

Strong winds push the thermocline deeper at one end of the lake basin.

The prevailing winds tend to funnel up the Windermere valley, blowing the surface water in a northerly direction. During the summer, when the lake is thermally stratified, a strong south to westerly wind can tilt the thermocline, which becomes deeper in the north of each basin and shallower in the south (the reverse happens with a northerly wind). Once the wind stops blowing, the thermocline tries to regain its original position but in doing so it undergoes a series of oscillations before equilibrium is restored. These internal movements within the lake are known as *seiches*. For organisms living freely in the water this is not too much of a problem because they can also move with the seiches, but where there are fixed abstraction points, such as intake pipes, water temperature and quality can change markedly over a short period of time.

The Windermere catchment

The northern part of the Windermere catchment comprises part of the Cumbrian massif, with hills rising to over seven hundred metres (2,300 feet). Bowfell, the Langdale Pikes and Fairfield are well-known landmarks in this part of the catchment. Towards the south, the hills are much gentler, rarely rising above three hundred metres – Gummers How (at 321 metres) is the highest point in the South Basin catchment. The natural vegetation of poor soils in the catchment is mixed woodland, dominated by sessile oak and ash, but much of the former forest has been cleared (Chapter 5). However, the original extent of the native woodland included those areas now dominated by bracken and extended to even higher levels on shallower soils (above the ecological limits of bracken). The original woodlands also dominated those areas that are now lowland wetlands or fields. Currently, moorland vegetation dominates the higher ground and bogs are readily formed in areas of poor natural drainage. Indeed, bogs of varying type can form in both upland and lowland situations – the most important determining factors are the amount of rainfall and ground conditions resulting in impeded drainage.

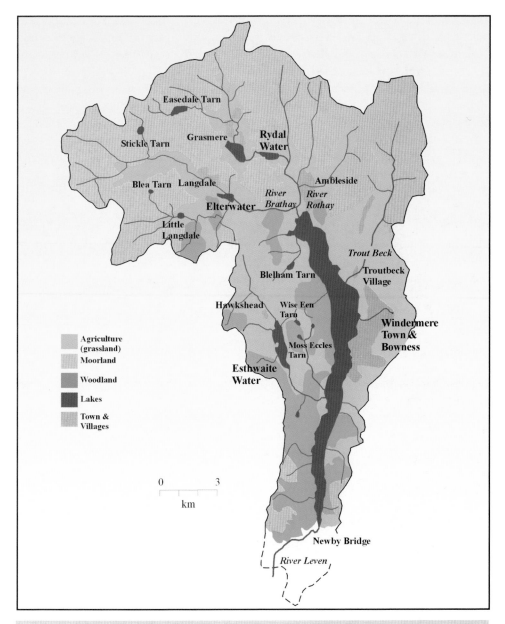

Principal land use in the Windermere catchment, based on data provided by the LDNPA.

The present landscape in the catchment of Windermere is strongly influenced by the impacts of agriculture and forestry. Approximately one-half of the area is grassland, providing pasture for cattle and sheep. As in other parts of the country, the use of inorganic fertilisers to promote the growth of pasture has become widespread, leading to a discernible effect on the water chemistry of the lake (Chapter 6). Beef cattle and dairy farming occurs in the south of the catchment (the dairy industry is now restricted to a handful of farms) but the higher ground is dominated by sheep production. The continuing practice is to turn the sheep out on to the open fells in the summer and keep them on the lower-lying pastures during the winter, but the details of these operations differ significantly with the breeds of sheep in the area (mainly Herdwicks, Swaledales and some Blue-faced Leicesters). Indeed, much of the typical 'Lakeland' landscape so appreciated by the visitor, such as stone walls and close-cropped fells, is the long-term result of farming livestock. In recent times there has been a gradual shift away from dairy to beef herds but the overall number of cattle has decreased. By comparison there has been an increase in the numbers of sheep in the Windermere catchment, but the current depressed state of the sheep-farming industry may well be a portent of further changes in the balance of agricultural practices within the catchment. However, such a change would require a major reformation of the European Common Agricultural Policy.

Modern forestry practices are more 'environmentally friendly' than they were earlier in the 20th century. In the Windermere catchment, woodlands and commercial forestry operations account for some ten percent of land usage.

Windermere South Basin, showing extensive woodland on the far western side of the lake.

There is some ancient, semi-natural woodland, although significant amounts of this were lost when coniferous trees were planted in the 1960s to the 1980s. In addition, the introduction of exotic trees was a feature of some of the larger houses and estates during the 19th century (Chapter 5). The National Trust is a significant landowner in the area and manages large tracts of woodland, principally along the western shore of the lake.

The main thoroughfare in the catchment is the A592, running along the eastern side of the Windermere valley, linking with the A591 at Windermere and the A590 near the outflow of the lake at Newby Bridge. These provide a direct route between the Furness area of Cumbria and the heart of the English Lake District.

The human dimension

To estimate the number of residents within the Windermere catchment at any particular time is not an easy task, partly because there is a transient influx of tourists and partly because the available population statistics are not organised on a catchment basis. From an analysis of the 1991 civil parish census figures (the latest available at the time of writing), the number of permanent residents in the catchment is around seventeen and a half thousand, of which the majority (about 9,000) live in the Windermere/Bowness conurbation. However, at the height of the tourist season, the number of people living in the Windermere catchment may exceed forty thousand as the many hotels and 'bed and breakfast' properties in the area are occupied. In addition there are twenty-two caravan and camp sites; these can accommodate a further two thousand visitors. Thus the principal present-day industries are agriculture (including forestry) and tourism; the latter (and its associated supporting industries such as retail and construction) is the mainstay of the local economy. Both agriculture and tourism have the potential to cause adverse impacts on the environment and this is an issue of growing importance, given the conservation status of the area. Quarrying for slates is now only a small industry (Chapter 5).

Conservation status of the Windermere catchment

The Lake District was designated as a National Park in 1951 and today is one of eleven National Parks in the UK. In England and Wales the purpose of National Park designation is to conserve and enhance the natural beauty, wildlife and cultural heritage of the National Park, and to promote opportunities for the understanding and enjoyment of the special qualities of the National Park. In pursuing these purposes the National Park Authority is required to seek to foster the economic and social well-being of local communities in the National Park, but without incurring significant expenditure.

The LDNPA works in partnership with other organisations, landowners and farmers to implement its statutory responsibilities (Chapter 8 gives further details of planning and management responsibilities within the Windermere catchment).

The LDNPA is also the planning authority for the National Park. The Lake District has also been designated by MAFF as an 'Environmentally Sensitive Area' (ESA). The ESA provides payments to help farmers manage their land in an environmentally sensitive way. This includes the sympathetic management of semi-natural habitats such as heather moorland and species-rich hay meadows, and the maintenance of cultural features such as walls, barns and other historic buildings. Finally, at this broader scale, the UK Government has identified the Lake District, Cumbria, as one of its priorities for nomination to UNESCO for World Heritage Status. The case is based primarily on the area's unique cultural landscape.

There is no specific conservation designation on Windermere as a whole, although the lake is classified as 'sensitive' under the Urban Waste Water Treatment Directive (Chapter 8). Low Wray Bay in the North Basin of Windermere is designated as a Site of Special Scientific Interest (SSSI) because it has an undisturbed sedimentary record. It is the 'type site' for the Windermere Interstadial (a warmer interlude during a period of cold climate) and, as such, is of national importance for studies of the last glaciation (Chapter 2). It also has a stony littoral region in shallow water, with a typical aquatic community of invertebrate animals, including various species of insects (Chapter 4).

Low Wray Bay on the north-western shore of Windermere, an important SSSI for studies on sediments.

Moss Eccles Tarn, an SSSI on Claife Heights, between Esthwaite Water and Windermere.

Apart from Low Wray Bay, the Windermere catchment contains twenty-three other SSSIs, several of which are directly related to aquatic habitats. Esthwaite Water, Elterwater, Little Langdale Tarn and Blelham Tarn (illustrated on pp. 21 to 23) and some of the tarns on Claife Heights, are all notified SSSIs with primary interests in aquatic flora and fauna. Additionally, Esthwaite North Fen and Blelham Bog are National Nature Reserves. In parallel with the existing SSSI system of site-based conservation, and in response to the Biodiversity Convention (signed at Rio as part of the Earth Summit in 1992), the UK has developed Action Plans for the conservation of key habitats and species. Within the Windermere catchment, the aquatic flora of Esthwaite Water is of particular interest with respect to the rare slender naiad *Najas flexilis,* a rather slim, submerged, freshwater plant. Last recorded in the lake in 1982 (probably now locally extinct), the slender naiad is a UK Priority Species under the UK Biodiversity Action Plan.

In summary, the Windermere catchment includes many sites of high conservation status. Thus, any development within the catchment must take serious account of such conservation issues if today's environment is to become tomorrow's heritage.

Lake-water chemistry

Before describing the biology and ecology of Windermere in the following chapter, we need to understand something of the lake's chemistry because this has a pervading influence on the organisms that are able to live there and on the overall productivity of the lake. The composition of solutes (dissolved salts) in the water is determined by the nature of the rain falling onto the catchment, its interaction with the soils, vegetation and underlying geology, and also by processes within the lake. The larger Cumbrian lakes form a natural series of relatively soft waters, ranging from those such as Wastwater where the total concentration of solutes is low, to Esthwaite Water in the Windermere catchment where the total concentration is almost three times higher. Windermere is towards the 'Esthwaite' end of this spectrum but the total solute content of Windermere is still low by British or world standards.

There are chemical differences between the North and South Basins of Windermere. The solute content of the South Basin is appreciably higher, due mainly to inflow from the Esthwaite Water sub-catchment, and differences in phosphorus levels have had a marked effect on the comparative ecology of the two parts of the lake. Much of the phosphorus in Windermere comes from treated sewage effluents that are discharged into both North and South Basins (details are given in Chapter 6). Another human impact can be seen in the levels of sodium chloride (common salt) which have increased over recent times, coincident with the use of salt for preventing ice formation on the roads in the catchment. The natural buffering capacity of the water in Windermere has been sufficient to minimise the impact of 'acid rain' deposition over the last two hundred years; more information is given in Chapter 5. Indeed, alkalinity has increased during the past fifty years; this may be partly caused by agricultural liming. Thus, both North and South Basins are normally neutral in reaction (pH slightly above 7.0). However, as algae and other plants (Chapter 4) grow in the lake, they take up carbon dioxide. When algae are present in large numbers, this uptake has the temporary effect of making the surface waters of the lake more alkaline during summer, because the lake-water does not have sufficient chemical 'buffering' capacity to prevent this happening for short periods of time. In general, water quality within the lake is high but increased concentrations of nutrients since the 1960s have provided cause for concern, particularly during the 1980s, and have stimulated remedial action on the main effluents discharging to the lake. These aspects are discussed in Chapters 6 and 7.

Chapter 4
The ecology of Windermere

Large, deep lakes like Windermere present a diversity of habitats for aquatic organisms and, over the lake's lifespan of some ten to twelve thousand years, all of these habitats have been occupied. Few lakes have been so intensively studied and it is therefore a sobering experience to realise that many aspects of Windermere's biology are virtually unexplored. This is particularly true for the benthic (bottom-dwelling) organisms in the deepest parts of the North and South Basins. Having said that, research *has* provided us with a great deal of information and, rather than musing on what we don't know, it is more profitable to consider the wealth of knowledge created by dedicated scientists and naturalists over the last seventy-five years. For convenience, the next few sections are organised by type of organism but it must be recognised that there is immense interaction between the different groups of animals, plants and microbes that live in Windermere and all are interdependent, to a lesser or greater extent. Rather than considering these links as a food chain it is, perhaps, more appropriate to think of them as a food *web*.

Phytoplankton

The term 'phytoplankton' is used to describe the unattached, microscopic algae dispersed in a waterbody. It is appropriate to consider these organisms first because they are one of the primary producers of the ecosystem, i.e., like all plants, they have the capacity to convert inorganic material to biological matter using the energy of sunlight. Normally occurring as single cells or small colonies, these algae have a bewildering variety of forms and well over a hundred species have been recorded in Windermere (almost certainly an underestimate of the true number). Freshwater planktonic algae are often responsible for making the water appear greenish or brown in colour. Although comparisons are not easy to make, the algal species in Windermere represent a significant proportion of the total number of phytoplankton species that occur in fresh waters worldwide, and the research on Windermere has probably done more than work elsewhere to help us understand the biology of this important group of organisms.

There is a marked seasonality in the timing and appearance of different algal species in the lake, and computer models, based on an understanding of algal growth in Windermere, have helped the water industry to predict, and avoid, problematic blooms of algae in other waterbodies. Moreover, the seasonal succession of different algal species is a useful model for the study of succession in more 'difficult' ecosystems: the seasonal cycle of phytoplankton in Windermere is the biological equivalent of a plant succession that occurs over many centuries in forest ecosystems!

Asterionella formosa is an abundant diatom in the phytoplankton of Windermere early in the spring of most years. In fact, during nearly all of fifty-five years continuous study, this diatom has been a dominant feature of the spring bloom of algae in the lake. It was discovered and named by Dr A. H. Hassall in the 19th century when investigating outbreaks of water-borne cholera and typhoid in London. He called it 'the little star of beautiful form'.

The first algae to appear early in the year are diatoms, characterised by their delicate outer shell of silica (a form of glass). These algae grow well at low temperatures and also tolerate the low light levels that occur early in the year, particularly when the lake is fully mixed. In Windermere the spring bloom of diatoms is usually dominated by *Asterionella formosa*, a colonial species that, as its name indicates, forms star-shaped clusters of cells. Diatom growth can be so prolific (in Windermere the recorded maximum concentration is over 11,000 cells per millilitre of water) that the diatoms eventually remove nearly all of the dissolved silica from the water, causing the population to collapse and die. Such a decrease in the number of algal cells in the water leads to a period of increased water clarity early in the summer, but this is soon followed by the growth of other species of algae.

The summer phytoplankton community in Windermere is usually composed of the so-called 'green' algae, many of which are surrounded by a mucilaginous sheath (a layer of slime). The exact function(s) of this sheath is not known but it does appear to aid suspension. This is important because these summer algae grow well at higher light intensities and therefore it is essential for them to remain in the upper, sunlit parts of the water column (the 'euphotic' zone).

Eventually (usually in late summer or early autumn) the summer community of predominantly green algae begins to run out of nutrients (phosphorus and nitrogen) and, as light intensity at the surface decreases with the onset of autumn, may be replaced by the 'blue-green' algae, or cyanobacteria.

The blue-green algae are relatively primitive plants, closely related to bacteria, which thrive in warm water but can grow at lower light levels. Moreover, certain forms can utilise atmospheric nitrogen as a nutrient source and some (but not *Tychonema bourrellyi* – see below) contain gas 'bubbles' (vacuoles) to prevent them from sinking. Some blue-green algae can also contain highly toxic substances but, in Windermere, the most abundant form in recent years has been a non-toxic, filamentous species, *Tychonema bourrellyi*. Sedimentation of this blue-green alga to the deeper parts of the lake during calm spells has resulted in loss of oxygen from the cooler water during late summer as the cells decompose, with potentially damaging consequences for the populations of Arctic charr (Chapter 6).

In most years the sequence of algal succession in Windermere is usually more complicated than the simple progression outlined above, because changing weather patterns regularly alter the conditions for plant growth in the lake and the different species of algae respond accordingly. As with many aspects of the lake's ecology, 'new' colonists appear from time to time. For example, the first record of the diatom *Aulacoseira islandica* in Windermere in 1987 might well be a response to increasing nutrient levels at that time. As primary producers the algae comprising the phytoplankton are important forms of food, either directly or indirectly, to other organisms within the lake. Thus they are essential to the overall health of the ecosystem but their excessive growth, resulting from enrichment of the lake by plant nutrients (eutrophication), can ultimately change the quality of the water.

A selection of green algae from the phytoplankton of Windermere, illustrating the wide diversity of forms.

Higher plants

The higher plants in Windermere form two basic communities: submerged plants, and those that grow, emerged or floating, around the margins of the lake. The term 'aquatic macrophyte' includes these higher plants, as well as a few large algae such as the blanket weed *Cladophora* (see Chapter 6 for information on blanket weed in Windermere). Detailed surveys of both macrophyte communities were undertaken in 1980, and in 1996 the submerged macrophytes were resurveyed. There have also been several less intensive studies prior to 1980. Windermere has the greatest diversity of aquatic macrophytes, including twenty-seven species of submerged macrophytes – of which the pondweeds (Potamogetonaceae) constitute the largest family. The six-stamened waterwort *Elatine hexandra* occurs in several shallow-water sites in both North and South Basins of the lake; this species is classified as scarce on a national basis. Inevitably, some changes in the macrophyte communities have occurred (over the last 150 years), the most obvious being the invasion of the lake by Canadian pondweed *Elodea canadensis*. This plant was first recorded in Windermere in 1847. In 1977 another member of the same genus, *Elodea nuttallii*, was recorded in South Cumbria for the first time. In 1980 both species were present in Windermere in reasonably similar amounts, but the 1996 survey shows that *E. nuttallii* has now largely replaced *E. canadensis* as the dominant aquatic macrophyte in deeper water. The distinctive *Littorella–Isoetes–Nitella* community of submerged macrophytes is still present on the western fringes of Windermere but its extent is diminished, compared with earlier descriptions. These changes are probably the result of increasing nutrient loads to the lake over the last forty years. Water clarity and resultant light penetration normally restricts the growth of submerged macrophytes to a depth of less than six metres, unless the water is exceptionally clear. Indeed, as algal populations increase, light penetration decreases and therefore there is an element of competition between the phytoplankton and the submerged macrophytes, not for nutrients but for light.

Windermere supports important examples of hydroseres (the transition from submerged aquatic macrophytes through emergent species and wet woodland to dry oak woodland). There are two main types on Windermere, characterised by their emergent vegetation and soils. In the soft-shore hydrosere the main emergent species is common reed *Phragmites australis* with, to a lesser extent, bulrush *Schoenoplectus lacustris*; these occur on fine silts and peat, usually in the vicinity of rivers and becks entering the lake. The stony-shore hydrosere, dominated by reed canary-grass *Phalaris arundinacea*, occurs on boulder clays. The wet woodland behind the reeds supports a wide variety of plants. Species of note in stony-shore hydroseres include globeflower *Trollius europaeus* and saw-wort *Serratula tinctoria*. Particularly good examples of hydroseres occur at White Cross Bay, Ecclerigg Bay, Landing Hole and Pull Wyke. Recent dieback of some of the *Phragmites* reedbeds around Windermere, notably at Grass Holme, is giving cause for concern

(Chapter 9) and research is now needed to understand the cause(s) of this dieback, before restoration can be attempted.

A reedbed in the North Basin of Windermere, with the common reed *Phragmites australis* in the foreground *(right)* and reed canary-grass *Phalaris arundinacea* in the background *(left)*.

Zooplankton

The other component of the free-floating, planktonic community in the lake is the zooplankton, made up of small invertebrate animals of various types. One of the most important members of the zooplankton community is *Daphnia hyalina-galeata*, a common 'water-flea'. Like many planktonic animals, water-fleas have adopted filter-feeding lifestyles and they strain small food particles, such as algae, from the water. Indeed, this grazing effect can exert a significant control over the numbers of planktonic algae in the lake at certain times of the year. The zooplankton occupies an important position in the overall food web of the lake because it is the main source of food for small fish and also for some larger fish such as the Arctic charr (see below). The zooplankton community in Windermere has not been studied so intensively as the phytoplankton community, but regular zooplankton samples have been taken and preserved, and certain key species have been monitored.

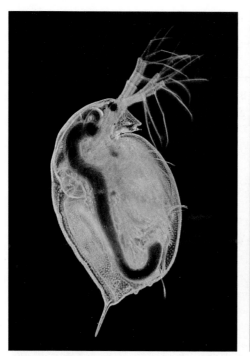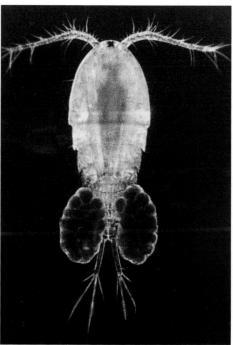

Two small planktonic crustaceans. *Left:* A cladoceran or water-flea (*Daphnia*). *Right:* A copepod (*Cyclops*) with two batches of developing eggs at the hind end of the body.

The two main components of the zooplankton are rotifers and crustaceans, the latter being further subdivided into cladocerans (water-fleas) and copepods. Twenty-eight species of rotifers and eleven species of planktonic crustaceans have been recorded in Windermere (these are almost certainly underestimates of the total number of species in the lake) and the overall community composition appears to have changed little during the last forty years. Indeed, we know from the sedimentary record (Chapter 2) that some zooplankton species have been permanent residents in the lake during the last ten thousand years! So far as we know only one crustacean, *Holopedium gibberum*, has been lost during recent times. However, there are marked seasonal changes in the abundance of zooplankton. Numbers normally reach a peak during May and June, at which time the number of larger animals may be as high as fifty per litre. Zooplankton abundance is higher in years when the weather is cool during the spring and early summer, and lower in years when the months of May and June are warm. The difference appears to be related to the timing and intensity of thermal stratification (Chapter 3) and can be correlated with annual changes in the position of the Gulf Stream as it tracks across the North Atlantic (Chapter 9).

Macro-invertebrates

The term 'aquatic macro-invertebrate' is used to describe invertebrate animals (i.e. all those without a backbone) that are easily visible to the naked eye and which normally occur on or in the bed of a river or lake. These include many insects that are well known as winged adults, when they emerge from the water to reproduce the next generation. The aquatic larval stages of four common insects are illustrated on pages 42 and 43. Many other kinds of macro-invertebrates live their entire lives in water (examples are shown on page 44).

A dragonfly waitings for its wings to harden after emerging from the skin (cuticle) of its aquatic nymph.

Above: Adult winged stages of a mayfly (*left*) and a caddisfly (*right*). *Below:* Aquatic larvae (nymphs) of a mayfly *(left,* with three tails or cerci) and a stonefly (*right,* two tails).

The least studied of all the animals in Windermere are the macro-invertebrates and these form two communities: those living in the shallows (the *littoral* community) and those living in the sediments of the deeper areas of the lake (the *benthic* community, dominated by midge larvae and aquatic worms). Some authorities refer to an intermediate community, the *sub-littoral*, at depths between one and ten metres, but little is known about these animals even though circumstantial evidence indicates that this may be the area of greatest invertebrate production.

 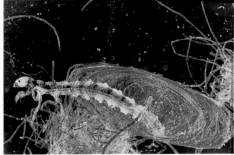

Two caddis larvae that build very different kinds of cases to protect the soft abdominal parts.

These communities include animals from quite different groups of invertebrates, including the aquatic stages of insects (larvae and nymphs), crustaceans, various types of worms, and molluscs. The lifestyles of this invertebrate fauna range from herbivorous (snails and many of the mayfly and stonefly larvae), through feeding on detritus (freshwater hog-louse and freshwater 'shrimps') to carnivorous (flatworms, some water-bugs and some water-beetles). As far as the author is aware, no complete species list has been attempted for the invertebrates living in Windermere but, given one report of forty-eight insect species alone occurring in just one type of habitat (the stony substratum), the total species count must be well in excess of a hundred. Of course, the macro-invertebrate fauna of a stony, waved-washed shore is very different from that, for example, of a reedbed or of a stand of submerged macrophytes in shallow water. In addition to providing a suitable habitat for water-bugs, dragonfly nymphs and a wide range of different mayfly species, plants also provide a refuge from fish and other carnivores.

It is impossible within the present text to cover all aspects of such a diverse group of animals and, therefore, a few selected examples will be used to illustrate particular topics. However, when considered as a group, macro-invertebrates are important components in the diets of several species of fish in Windermere, particularly (but not exclusively) those frequenting the shallower areas of the lake.

In Windermere, aquatic insects are well represented by mayflies, stoneflies, caddisflies and midges (chironomids). Hatches of the large mayfly *Ephemera danica* usually occur in June but other species of insect hatch into adults at different times of the year. For example, large hatches of the non-biting midges *Chironomus plumosus* and *Chironomus anthracinus* occur during April and May, rising from the deeper parts of the lake, and these attract feeding trout and charr to the surface of the lake in the evenings. The darkish grey or black adults dance in swirling mating swarms, often at the edges of the lake, and they may be seen performing alongside the road at Ferry Nab.

Examples of six macro-invertebrates that are fully aquatic throughout their life-cycles. *Top row:* Freshwater shrimp (*left*) and freshwater hog-louse (*right*). *Middle row:* Flatworm (*left*) and ostracod crustacean (*right*). *Bottom row*: Gastropod snails (*left*) and pea mussel (*right*).

The relatively large larvae (1 to 2 cm in length) of *Chironomus* are sometimes called 'bloodworms' because they contain the red pigment haemoglobin (as in humans). This enables the larvae to survive in the sediments of the deepest part of the lake, even when oxygen levels are too low for most other organisms. In contrast the aquatic larvae of the minute biting midge *Culicoides* are commonest in small lakes, pools and boggy areas in the Windermere catchment. Only the female bites, obtaining blood proteins required for making her eggs. The tiny grey flies are scarcely visible (appropriately called 'no-see-ums' in North America) but their painful bites can make warm summer evenings a misery for anyone near water; they are particularly numerous in western Scotland but all too common in the Lake District. Their attacks are usually blamed on the much larger gnats and mosquitoes, a few of which also bite, and 'clegs', which adopt a stealthy approach and are noticed only when they inflict a very painful bite!

The carnivorous aquatic larva of the alderfly *Sialis lutaria* prefers silty areas around the margins of the lake. It pupates just above the waterline and hatches into the adult fly in April and May. Long-term records of the appearance of adults on the shoreline of Windermere, backed by detailed experimental evidence, show that the date of hatching is temperature-dependent and the analysis of such valuable data-sets can be used to detect the first signs of environmental change (Chapter 9).

One particularly interesting and rare stonefly in Windermere is *Capnia bifrons*, an almost completely ovoviviparous insect – i.e. the fertilised eggs are retained internally by the female and laid when about to hatch. It has been suggested that this may be an adaptation to combat low water temperatures (most of the embryonic development occurs while the egg is still within the body of the adult female) and, therefore, this species may well be a glacial relict within the lake.

Other invertebrates are relative newcomers to Windermere. The freshwater crustacean amhipod *Crangonyx pseudogracilis* was first recorded in the lake in 1960 by a group of students and is now widespread in shallow water. Originally from North America, this species probably arrived in the UK in the bilge water of ships (although some prefer the hypothesis that it came across in consignments of ornamental aquarium plants), but soon established itself in the fresh waters of this country. In Windermere it cohabits with another amphipod – which it superficially resembles – the native freshwater shrimp *Gammarus pulex*. Similarly, the introduced freshwater hog-louse *Asellus aquaticus* cohabits with the native *Asellus meridianus* and may be slowly replacing the latter. Another successful colonist is a freshwater snail, the gastropod *Potamopyrgus jenkinsi*. Originally found in a brackish marsh in the Thames Estuary in 1889, this small snail colonised much of England and Wales within thirty years. Whether this is a mutant brackishwater species or an antipodean colonist (which should be called *Potamopyrgus antipodarum*) is still subject to conjecture, but there is no doubt that since its first appearance in Windermere in 1936, at Whitecross Bay, it has been slowly extending its range within the lake. In the late 1980s a species of helminthid water-beetle, *Oulimnius troglodytes*, was recorded for the first time; another species, *O. tuberculatus*, has been present on stony shores for many decades.

In general, many of the observed changes in the macro-invertebrate communities in Windermere reflect the trend towards increasing nutrient levels and organic enrichment in the lake, especially in the South Basin.

Fish populations in Windermere

Arctic charr

Arctic charr female (*above*) and male (*below*) in spawning livery.

The Arctic charr *Salvelinus alpinus* is, arguably, the most important species in the lake because it is of conservation interest and also forms the basis of a small, semi-commercial fishery (Chapter 5). It is a cold-water species (as its name implies) and has the most northerly distribution of any freshwater fish. The populations in Windermere are at the extreme south of their range and, therefore, they are particularly sensitive to environmental change. The species survives in Windermere as a glacial relict because the lake is deep and, during the summer months, there is ample cold water in both North and South Basins (for a description of thermal stratification in the lake, see Chapter 3). Today, charr populations at latitudes above sixty degrees north are frequently 'anadromous', i.e. like salmon, they migrate to feed in the sea. However, at such high latitudes the sea is too cold for the fish to survive during the winter months and they have to return to fresh water in the autumn. Interestingly, although the Windermere charr is now an exclusively freshwater fish, it still retains a physiological 'memory' of its original migratory behaviour and, during the spring months, can be adapted to dilute sea water.

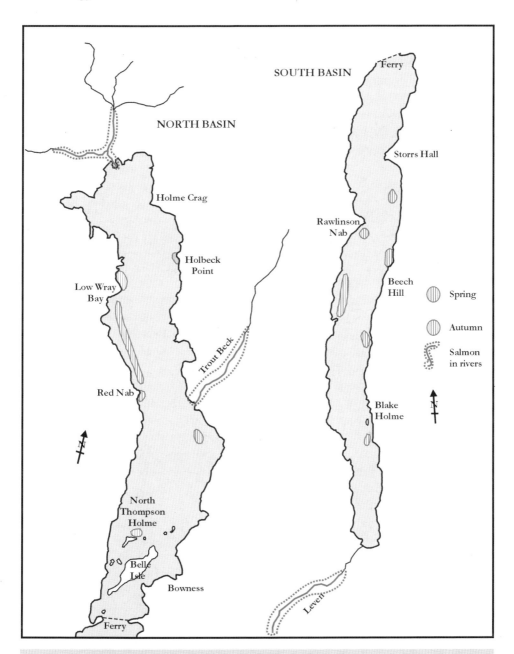

The main spawning sites for Arctic charr in Windermere and Atlantic salmon in rivers of the catchment.

The Windermere charr populations are unusual in that they spawn at two different times of the year. Some fish, the so-called 'autumn spawners', lay their eggs in relatively shallow water (1 to 3 metres) at certain sites around the shore of the lake; 'spring spawners' lay their eggs in much deeper water.

In autumn-spawning charr, spawning takes place between October and December and the eggs are laid on areas of gravel that are without any vegetation. One population even spawns in a large pool at the lower end of the River Brathay, a main inflow to the lake. The 'spring spawners' lay their eggs at fifteen to twenty metres during January to April. Tagging experiments have shown that each population is faithful to its own spawning site and this has resulted in a degree of genetic divergence between autumn spawners and spring spawners. It is even possible that each spawning site has its own genetic stock of fish. There are subtle structural differences in the gills of autumn and spring spawners but it requires an expert to recognise them. During the rest of the year, these different stocks of fish mix quite freely within both basins of the lake, only to return again to their own spawning sites to breed. During the spawning season, the fish (males in particular) develop a spectacular vermillion colour on the undersides of the body as they compete with each other for suitable partners and for access to the spawning gravels. Indeed, the name 'charr' derives from the Gaelic for 'red-belly'.

As a cold-water species, the charr is relatively slow-growing and long-lived, with some Windermere charr exceeding twelve years of age. Indeed, it may take a fish some four to six years to become sexually mature. In general, the autumn spawning fish initially produce the largest offspring but the spring spawners ultimately exhibit the fastest growth rate, particularly those feeding in the South Basin. During the summer months the fish are pelagic (living in the open waters of the lake) and feed voraciously on zooplankton, particularly cladocerans (see the section on zooplankton, p. 40). However, during the earlier part of the year, bloodworms (the larvae of non-biting chironomid midges; p. 44) and their resultant pupae form an important part of the diet of the charr and the fish also feed avidly on their own eggs during the spawning season(s). Broadly speaking, the feeding habits of the charr do not overlap with those of the other species of fish in Windermere and, therefore, there is little competition for food. Occasional reports of charr feeding on young fish (particularly perch fry) have been verified by the author – these reports are of interest because, in at least one Scottish loch, there is evidence of a distinct sub-population of charr that have resorted to eating other fish. Population estimates are difficult to make in a large and complex lake like Windermere, but the total number of adult charr in the lake is probably several hundred thousand. Chapters 6 and 7 give accounts of recent changes in the Windermere charr populations, following a decline and subsequent improvement in water quality.

Perch

In terms of absolute numbers, the perch *Perca fluviatilis* is the most abundant of the larger species of fish in Windermere. Population estimates have varied, as the numbers of fish have waxed and waned within the lake, but at their peak (before

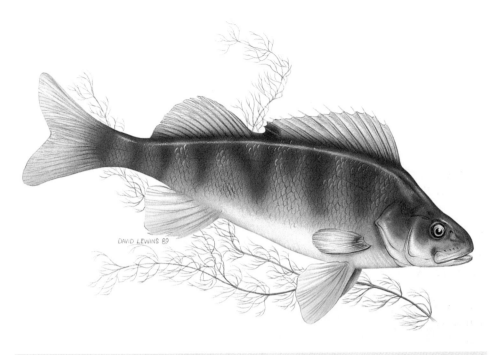

An original drawing of a Windermere perch.

the 1940s and also again in the late 1950s and early 1960s) some five to six million adult perch inhabited Windermere. Current estimates are about half that number. When scientific studies of the perch began in the 1930s, the population consisted of overcrowded, stunted fish, but the impact of the war-time perch fishery (Chapter 5) reduced the overall number of fish and, at the same time, increased their growth rates and final body size.

Perch have a marked seasonal migration in Windermere, occupying the littoral and sub-littoral regions of the lake (down to a depth of 10 metres, see p. 42) in the summer months but moving to deeper water (between 18 and 27 metres) in the winter. Their return to shallower waters towards the end of April coincides with sexual maturation, and spawning takes place in May. The fish lay their egg masses on rooted vegetation, particularly *Elodea,* at depths of about three metres around the margins of the lake. The initial diet of the newly-hatched perch is zooplankton but, as the fish grow, they feed on macro-invertebrates and other fish (sticklebacks, minnows and young of their own species). Survival of young perch is strongly influenced by temperature, with warm summers ensuring strong recruitment of the young fish into the population. The diet of the smaller perch changes during the winter months, moving away from macro-invertebrates to some of the smaller zooplankton. For the larger fish, an increasing proportion have empty stomachs during the winter months. A small percentage of the overall perch population in

Windermere adopts an exclusively piscivorous habit (feeding largely on young perch) and these animals can grow to a weight in excess of a kilogram (well over 2 lbs).

In 1976, a major catastrophe hit the Windermere perch population in the form of a disease that wiped out over ninety-eight percent of the adult population. Never fully diagnosed at the time, the causative organism was probably a variant form of a bacterium that causes a fish disease known as furunculosis. Infected fish developed lesions on their flanks that readily became colonised by pathogenic fungi, ultimately resulting in the death of the fish. There was circumstantial evidence that this disease had spread to the Lake District from the south-east of England, taking several years to reach Windermere where it had a devastating effect. The rapid population decline of the perch resulted in increased growth rates in the survivors (as, indeed, occurred in survivors from the perch-trapping operations of the Second World War – see Chapter 5), a shift in the sex ratio towards females (possibly indicating greater disease-induced mortality of the male fish) and a reduction in the normal lifespan of the fish. In some way there had been a 'physiological acceleration' of the fish towards rapid growth, earlier sexual maturation and reduced life expectancy. Such a response may be a natural mechanism by which the species re-populates, following a rapid decline in numbers. It took more than a decade before the sex ratios returned to 'normal' but the population has not yet returned to its former, high pre-disease values.

Pike

A young pike 'hovering' in the water, prior to attack.

Local angler David Bailey with a magnificent 30lb pike caught in Windermere.

The pike *Esox lucius* is a top predator in Windermere, with a fully-grown female fish attaining a weight of some sixteen kilograms (over 35 lbs) at fifteen years of age. A fish of this size is quite capable of swallowing whole, large adult perch, charr and trout, but some of the popular accounts of the appetite of pike are a little exaggerated. To survive and grow, a pike needs to eat something like four times its own body weight per year – energy conversion in this species is extremely efficient because its principal diet is one of fish. The pike is built for ambush and sudden attack, with the large dorsal fin and tail fin acting in concert to generate rapid acceleration of the fish through the water. The large mouth, armed with extremely sharp teeth, ensures that prey rarely escape from its jaws. Although the pike is normally a somewhat sedentary fish, tagging studies on Windermere have shown that they do move between the North and South Basins during the course of a season (possibly in small groups) but tend to return to their 'home territory' during the spawning season.

The pike spawn in February in shallow reedy areas around the margins of the lake and initially feed on zooplankton and small invertebrates but, as soon as they attain a length of just three centimetres, they become exclusively fish eaters. Female pike eventually grow more rapidly than males and, like perch, their growth rate and recruitment into the population is influenced by temperature. Pike do particularly well in their first year when the late summer and autumn months are relatively warm.

Pike numbers in Windermere have fluctuated markedly over the last seventy years and declined following perch disease (see above) – numbers have subsequently increased again and the current adult population is somewhere between five and ten thousand fish. At the end of the Second World War a culling experiment was undertaken to see if removal of large numbers of pike would protect their prey species, particularly the charr and trout. The results of this study have become something of a scientific 'classic', illustrating that nature does not always work in the way you might expect. Catching fish in gill-nets and removing the largest fish had an immediate effect by reducing adult pike in the population but the numbers soon recovered and actually increased. The pike population now consisted of more, younger, faster-growing fish and the total predation pressure on the trout and charr had increased. The cannibalistic tendencies of this species meant that the largest pike had been controlling the numbers of smaller pike in the population and removal of the large fish had released a 'brake' on the population. Gill-nets are still used to monitor the pike population in the lake but the numbers of fish taken for scientific purposes are small and do not have a discernible impact on the adult population.

Trout

The species *Salmo trutta* includes the resident brown trout, migratory sea trout and an intermediate type that drifts between fresh water and the brackish water of the estuary (sometimes referred to as 'slob' trout). Unfortunately our scientific knowledge of the Windermere trout is somewhat limited and we would like to know more about it. Unlike the fish considered thus far, the Windermere trout do not spawn in the lake but in the tributaries running into it. The spawning migration from the lake occurs in late November, usually during a spate (flood), and the females normally spawn and return to the lake within twenty-four hours. The males, on the other hand, may stay in the spawning stream for several days to fertilise other females, and a proportion of the spawning males actually may be resident stream fish that have never lived in the lake. An unpublished study of the genetics of the young trout in two of the inflowing streams of Windermere, Wilfin Beck and Scandale Beck, suggests that each stream has its own, unique genetic stock of fish.

The young trout hatch during the following spring and feed in the stream for one, two or three years before moving out into the lake. The majority of the young fish are two years old when they first enter Windermere. Mathematical models describing the growth of young trout indicate that whilst in the streams the fish have ample food and their growth rate is largely determined by water temperature. Once in the lake the young fish occupy the littoral zone (see p. 42) where their growth rate is usually accelerated. In addition to occupying the littoral zone some trout feed in the open water of the lake, but it is not known whether these two components of the population are genetically distinct. Fish from around the shoreline often look physically different from those of the open water, with a tendency towards a yellow colouration and red spots (locally known as 'yellow bellies') compared with the silver flanks and black spots of the pelagic trout. However, the appearance of a fish can be strongly influenced by its environment

Above: A typical brown trout with golden flanks and red spots, from the shoreline of Windermere.
Below: A silvery trout with black spots, from open water in Windermere.

and it would require a sophisticated molecular, genetic analysis of the two types of trout to determine whether these differences are genetic or environmental. The situation is further complicated by the fact that there are seasonal variations in the proportions of the trout population inhabiting the two environments, with fewer fish in the littoral zone during the winter months. At this time the littoral fish feed primarily on molluscs and crustaceans, switching to insect larvae and pupae during spring and early summer, and exploiting terrestrial insects (taken at the surface of the water) during summer and early autumn. The eggs of charr also feature in the diet of Windermere trout at the relevant time of year (see above). When in the open water of the lake, the trout feed on chironomid midge larvae and pupae and may, like charr, take planktonic crustaceans. A small proportion of Windermere trout become exclusively piscivorous and these fish grow to a larger size; trout up to fifteen pounds in weight (6 kg) have been caught in the lake.

Definitive population estimates of the resident Windermere trout have never been undertaken but an early study in the 1930s estimated the littoral population to be in the region of twelve thousand fish. Anecdotal evidence suggests that trout numbers in the lake have declined and this is partially supported by a reduction in the numbers of spawning fish noted for one spawning stream at Great Oaks Wood in the 1970s. The Environment Agency is keen to work with local anglers to try to obtain information on changes in the trout population of Windermere.

Sea trout migrate up the River Leven and through Windermere to spawn in the larger tributaries such as the River Brathay, River Rothay and Trout Beck. Often difficult to distinguish from large lake trout, our knowledge of the sea trout population of Windermere is largely restricted to the analysis of catch statistics in the River Leven fishery (both nets and rods). Annual sea trout catches between 1987 and 1999 have varied between fewer than fifty fish in 1993, to more than two hundred and fifty fish in 1988. No long-term trend is apparent in the Leven data, although national catch statistics for sea trout show an overall decline during this period.

Atlantic salmon

Like sea trout, the Atlantic salmon *Salmo salar* also feeds out at sea and then migrates into the Windermere catchment to spawn. The main spawning sites (see p. 47) are in the River Leven, just downstream from Newby Bridge, in the lower reaches of the Rothay and Brathay river system, and in Trout Beck. Genetic analysis of young salmon (parr) from the three spawning areas indicates that each stock is genetically distinct and little or no interbreeding occurs amongst them, a finding that has important implications for the management of salmon in Windermere. The growth of young salmon in the River Leven is also significantly faster than for fish in other spawning streams, probably because of slightly higher temperatures during the main growing season. After one to three years in the spawning stream (usually 2 years), the young salmon parr undergoes a dramatic metamorphosis into the smolt and migrates downstream to Morecambe Bay and thence to the open sea. This transformation from parr to smolt effectively changes the fish from an

Atlantic salmon migrating upstream to spawn.

aggressive, territorial, freshwater fish to a shoaling, seawater fish. Smolts from the River Leven can simply drift down to the sea but those from the headwaters of the catchment must actively traverse the whole length of the lake. The fish then feed at sea for a length of time anywhere between six months and three years.

Because juvenile salmon are recognisable from juvenile trout, we have a little more information on salmon populations than we do on the sea trout populations (where it is difficult to distinguish juvenile migratory fish from juvenile resident fish). There are concerns that the River Leven spawning site is relatively restricted, causing fish to disturb existing eggs by 'over-cutting' the redds, and there is also evidence of high mortality at the fry stage. Moreover, in Trout Beck there is good genetic evidence indicating that some trout and salmon interbreed to produce hybrids. Nothing is known about the viability of such offspring, but hybrid production could indicate that the spawning areas for the two species are both restricted and overlapping. Analysis of the salmon catch statistics for the River Leven shows a marked decline in catches during the 1990s, with an all-time low of only twenty-six fish caught in 1999. This trend is in line with national catch statistics for salmon but the rate of decline in the Leven might indicate some additional, local problems.

Eel

Our knowledge of the biology of the eel *Anguilla anguilla* in the Windermere catchment is largely confined to studies carried out in the 1940s. Like the trout (see above) the eel does not spawn in the lake, but in this case its spawning grounds are some four thousand miles away in the Sargasso Sea on the other side of the Atlantic Ocean! It takes approximately two years (estimates range between 1 and 3 years) for the larval eels to drift back to UK coastal waters on the ocean currents, where they transform themselves, firstly into transparent 'glass' eels and then, as skin pigmentation begins to develop, into elvers. The upstream migration of elvers in the River Leven usually occurs in April as the young eels make their way into the rivers and lakes of the Windermere catchment. Once in fresh water, the eels feed and grow until it is time for them to make the reverse journey across the Atlantic to spawn.

Eels stay a remarkably long time (up to 19 years) in the Windermere catchment, where they feed and grow. The eels in the lake feed largely on freshwater molluscs, aquatic insect larvae and the freshwater shrimp *Gammarus*, whereas eels feeding in the rivers are more reliant on chironomid larvae and mayfly nymphs. Surprisingly few fish have been found in the stomachs of eels in the Windermere catchment. Eels are opportunistic feeders (for example they will eat perch if trapped together in the same perch trap) and their diet probably reflects the dominant food organisms within each waterbody. Female eels grow much larger than males and a large Windermere fish may weigh almost five pounds (2.3 kilograms). Whilst in fresh water the eels are referred to as yellow eels, reflecting the colouration of their flanks and belly, but after a period of between eight and nineteen years in the lake or river, they undergo a transformation into silver eels. As well as an obvious colour change, the silver eel is characterised by a narrowing of the head and an enlargement of its eyes as it prepares for the arduous migration back to the spawning grounds. Silver eels migrate downstream in autumn but very few male fish are seen on this downstream migration from the Windermere catchment. It is possible that the smaller males normally feed and grow in the estuarine or coastal environment, rarely penetrating deep into fresh water.

Other species of fish

In addition to the species described above, Windermere is home to the minnow *Phoxinus phoxinus*, bullhead *Cottus gobio*, stone loach *Barbatula barbatula* and three-spined stickleback *Gasterosteus aculeatus*. At least two of the three British species of lamprey (the river lamprey *Lampetra fluviatilis* and the sea lamprey *Petromyzon marinus*) spawn in the catchment and there have been occasional reports of cyprinid fish (rudd *Scardinius erythrophthalmus*, bream *Abramis brama* and tench *Tinca tinca*).

Esthwaite Water, within the Windermere catchment, has a relatively good head of rudd and roach (and their hybrids occur in Priest Pot) and recent reports of an expanding population of roach *Rutilus rutilus* in Windermere will be considered further in Chapter 9.

Waterfowl

In the context of this section, the term 'waterfowl' is used rather loosely to include birds whose main habitat is aquatic.

Wintering species

More than a thousand ducks, geese and swans are resident on Windermere throughout the year but this number rises to more than two and a half thousand during the winter as birds arrive from their nesting grounds in Scandinavia and eastern Europe. Windermere ranks above all the other Lake District lakes for the overall number of its wintering wildfowl and is nationally important for a number of species. Almost inevitably, the mallard *Anas platyrhynchos*, with its ready tolerance of humans, is the most abundant species. Mallard numbers are highest during the winter months (about 2,000 maximum) as migrants move in from the continent. These winter visitors are much more sensitive to disturbance than the resident birds. Nationally important numbers of tufted duck *Aythya fuligula* arrive in October from Iceland and most leave again in April. Windermere is also nationally important for wintering coot *Fulica atra*. Perhaps the most important winter migrant on the lake (from Norway and Sweden) is the goldeneye *Bucephala clangula*. Some two percent of the goldeneye population in the UK (more than 300 birds) spend the winter on Windermere.

A goldeneye drake wintering on Windermere. Like the tufted duck and coot, goldeneye dive repeatedly to catch small crustaceans, molluscs and other invertebrates.

All five species of British gulls roost on Windermere during the winter months and the numbers of cormorant *Phalacrocorax carbo* have increased significantly over recent years. Other waterfowl present over the winter include pochard *Aythya ferina*, mute swan *Cygnus olor*, goosander *Mergus merganser* and great crested grebe *Podiceps cristatus*.

Breeding birds

The numbers of mute swan have increased during recent years but their nests are still prone to disturbance and to flooding, as lake-levels fluctuate. Coot and mallard are plentiful and, during the summer, red-breasted mergansers *Mergus serrator* now breed on the lake. The larger of the two sawbills, the goosander, is also a frequent visitor, nesting in woodlands around the lake. Greylag geese *Anser anser* and Canada geese *Branta canadensis* have increased in numbers during recent years, the latter species to nuisance proportions.

A flock of Canada geese (and one greylag) on the shore of Windermere.

Cormorants, goosanders and mergansers are the focus of an unresolved dispute between the angling fraternity and bird conservationists because of the birds' piscivorous habits. A study of the feeding pattern of young mergansers on Windermere demonstrated that they were capable of eating prodigious numbers (up to 20,000) of young-of-the-year perch during their first growing season, but there is little evidence that this level of predation in Windermere has had any significant impact on recruitment of perch into the adult population (see p. 49).

One of the major ornithological issues on Windermere is the loss of undisturbed habitat. The decline of reedbeds (Chapter 9) is of particular concern in relation to shoreline nesting sites, and the extension of boating activity throughout the winter months is seen by some as a threat to the over-wintering migrants on the lake.

Microbes in Windermere

In the context of this section, the term 'microbe' refers to bacteria, fungi and protozoa. Microbial activity is responsible for much of the recycling that occurs in the lake, converting dead organic material back into its constituent parts and thereby putting carbon, in particular, back into the food web. We have seen above (p. 50) that, in addition to their normal saprophytic lifestyle (i.e. feeding on dead organic matter), some aquatic fungi can also act as pathogens on diseased fish. Moreover, some specialised freshwater fungi, belonging to a group called the chytrids, are parasitic on algal cells and, under extreme circumstances, can bring about the collapse of algal blooms, even when nutrients are still available. The bacteria and protozoa are the recyclers *par excellence*, with different groups of organisms capable, collectively, of surviving and metabolising under every conceivable environmental condition in the lake. Thus some microbial groups thrive under conditions of high oxygen levels whereas others only flourish when oxygen is absent, even in the presence of toxic gases such as hydrogen sulphide, which would kill most other organisms. There is a theory that all free-living bacteria are ubiquitous at a global scale; i.e. if suitable environmental conditions develop, there will always be a group of bacteria available to exploit these conditions. Bacteria are normal components of the biology of a healthy lake and play a crucial role in the recycling of carbon, nitrogen, phosphorus, sulphur and other chemical elements within the lake, an activity sometimes referred to as bio-geochemical cycling. In many cases they work in close harmony with protozoa (unicellular, animal-like organisms), so much so that in some instances the bacteria actually live within the body of the protozoan. A good example is provided by the ciliate *Metopus palaeformis*, a protozoan that has been isolated from Windermere. This particular protozoan contains large numbers of a bacterium known as *Methanobacterium* (p. 60).

The protozoan can only survive under anaerobic conditions (i.e. in the absence of oxygen) where it obtains its energy by fermenting organic matter. This fermentation process has a toxic by-product, hydrogen gas, which accumulates in the body of the protozoan. However, the bacteria living within the single-celled ciliate use the hydrogen for their own metabolism, converting it to methane, which then diffuses harmlessly away. Therefore both partners in this consortium benefit – an elegant example of symbiosis at the microbial scale.

Not all interactions between bacteria and protozoa are mutually beneficial. Indeed, bacteria constitute an essential food source for most protozoa, thereby bridging an important gap in the food web. Small protozoa are eaten by larger protozoa and these are eaten by numerous planktonic animals (rotifers and crustaceans); the latter organisms are then preyed upon by fish. Thus microbial activity is crucial in linking the breakdown of organic matter to the uptake of material at the lower end of the food chain, the so-called 'microbial loop'.

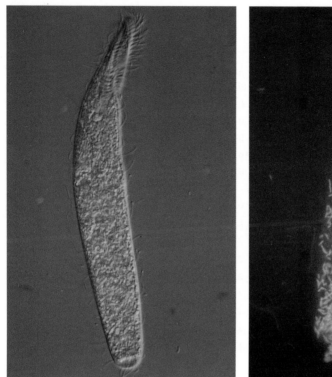 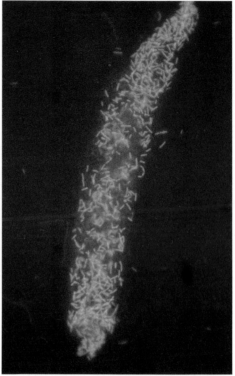

Symbiosis between a ciliate and a bacterium (*Methanobacterium*). *Left: Metopus palaeformis;* the mouth of the ciliate is at the top of the picture. *Right:* under fluorescent light the rod-shaped bacteria are visible in the body of the ciliate.

Final comment

In this chapter we have briefly considered microscopic organisms in the plankton of Windermere, moved through larger plants and animals, and then returned to the smallest organisms of all, the microbes. Whether minute or large, all are linked within a complex series of interdependent hierarchies, forming a food web in which all organisms play a key role. Although some species, such as the Arctic charr, have a high conservation profile, their presence and the overall health of the lake is a function of interaction amongst all of its components. Over time, changes in the flora and fauna occur naturally and some may be inevitable; like most lakes, Windermere exists in a state of delicate balance in which organisms tend to wax and wane in numbers and extent. Nevertheless, human intervention is sometimes required to maintain a form of generally acceptable *status quo* in order to redress the balance where it is clear that components of the lake ecosystem are seriously threatened by human activities both within the lake and on its catchment.

Chapter 5
Human influence

The landscape that emerged from the last glaciation (Chapter 2), although initially barren, would have been rapidly vegetated and colonised; contemporary studies of modern glaciated areas reveal a surprisingly diverse and active human culture living in close proximity to ice sheets. In the Lake District, boulder clays, lateral moraines and other glacial debris provided the mineral basis for developing soils in the area and subsequent plant growth gradually contributed the organic component. At some time around thirteen to twelve thousand years ago, the climate became milder and trees appeared. However a colder period intervened, during which the waning glaciers re-advanced in the valley heads before finally retreating and disappearing altogether. During the colder spell there was a shift in the vegetation away from trees and towards scrub, before further amelioration of the climate resulted in colonisation by hardy birch woodland, followed by hazel, and then oak and elm appeared. At the end of the period of afforestation, the vegetation of the Lake District probably consisted of predominantly oak woodland on the better-drained slopes. Ash would have been common on the limestone and in the valley bottoms, with alder and willow in the wetter areas. True mountain vegetation would have been present above the tree-line and on the highest summits.

Human impact on the Windermere catchment

We have seen from Chapter 3 how important it is to consider not only the lake but also its catchment, because changes in land use can have a significant impact on both the amount and the quality of water entering the lake. This chapter now describes the main stages of human settlement of the Lake District, making specific reference to the Windermere catchment, when possible. Particular attention is given to agricultural practices because they have such a direct influence on land use but, during the later periods of human settlement, industry has also left its mark. What then follows is a summary of some of the more direct impacts of people on the lake itself.

Stone Age settlement

It is conventional to divide the 'Stone Age' into three main periods: the Palaeololithic (2.5 million years ago to about 12,000 BC), the Mesolithic (12,000 to about 4,000 BC) and the Neolithic (4,000 to 2,400 BC). These dates are approximate and vary over different parts of Europe. During the last glaciation the ice-covered Cumbrian dome was an extremely inhospitable environment for human survival and Palaeolithic (Old Stone Age) man would have found little attraction in the area compared with the more amenable climate in areas further south. Evidence of any earlier existence in Cumbria will have been largely obliterated by glacial activity but there are some Palaeolithic remains from caves in the Carboniferous limestone in south Cumbria. Artefacts of Mesolithic (Middle Stone Age) man can be found in the western coastal plain, where the availability of flint (for making tools) along the shoreline was an undoubted attraction. The origin of this flint has been the subject of much speculation (flint is a form of silica that only occurs in chalk deposits), but the discovery of a chalk reef under the Irish Sea is one possible explanation. Coastal zones and estuaries were also attractive because of food resources (birds and fish) and boat transport.

Mesolithic man moved into the British Isles from Northern Europe as a nomadic food collector, hunter and fisherman, but was largely restricted to the periphery of the Lake District (although a few Mesolithic flints have been found from more central areas). His only tools were made of flint, bone, wood and plant fibres; consequently he did not have the technical ability to make any significant impact on the environment of the newly-formed lakes or their catchments.

The Neolithic culture initially developed in the eastern Mediterranean region and then spread northwards, possibly arriving in Cumbria via Ireland. In something of a cultural revolution, man had developed the capability to fashion, sharpen and polish stone into much more effective tools than those of Mesolithic man; the Windermere catchment was an important area for the manufacture of stone tools, with a major 'axe factory' on the screes below Pike of Stickle, in Great Langdale.

Site of Neolithic axe-factory below Pike of Stickle, at about 500 metres (1,800 ft) above sea level. At this altitude, axes probably were roughly fashioned in spring and summer, before transport to the coast for final polishing. The fine-grained volcanic rocks on the screes flake and chip conchoidally (i.e. in shell-like fashion), yielding sharp edges.

The volcanic rocks in this area (Chapter 2) flake and chip in a manner similar to flint and, therefore, are suitable for making tools. It seems likely that axe heads were roughly fashioned on the screes themselves (evident from the numerous flakes and a few, rejected, misshapen axe heads) but were finished elsewhere. The finishing procedure involved polishing and sharpening, processes that probably occurred in the coastal areas (such as Ravenglass), where sandstone and sand were plentiful for such purposes. The finished axes originating from Great Langdale can be readily identified petrologically (i.e. from the composition of the rock) and have been found in significant numbers as far away as Hampshire and the Thames valley. Clearly, the axe factory in the Windermere catchment was the centre of an important, early export industry.

Neolithic man was less of a nomad than his predecessors and introduced into Britain the cultivation of crops and herding of animals, as well as domestic crafts such as weaving and making pottery. This early agriculture required the clearance of small forest plots and the stone axes were perfectly capable of such work. Indeed, a modern experiment in Denmark demonstrated that, using similar tools, three men could clear six hundred square yards of birch scrub in four hours! A degree of lowland forest clearance occurred some four and a half thousand years ago but upland clearance occurred progressively over a much longer period (see below). Perhaps the most obvious legacy of late Neolithic man in the region is the network of large stone (megalithic) circles. Their distribution towards the periphery of the Cumbrian dome (with the singular exception of Castlerigg, near Keswick) supports the view that Neolithic culture was more suited to the hospitable, lower-lying areas. It is thought that the stone circle was more than a burial ground and probably represents some form of ceremonial or religious temple.

Bronze and Iron Ages

The next major event in human development was the ability to extract and work metals. The ability to use copper developed in the late Neolithic and this was followed by the production of bronze, a harder alloy of copper and tin. Bronze Age man, like his predecessors, was involved in rearing stock and cultivating grain and, undoubtedly, was also a hunter. Thus he continued the process of deforestation and penetrated further into the heart of the Lake District, evident from the distribution of Bronze Age barrows, cairns and remains of settlements on the lower fells. Such a change in distribution might be the result of increased population pressures. Some two thousand years ago the Iron Age was well advanced in the south of England and this technology must have influenced the native Cumbrians to some extent before the next major historical event, the Roman invasion.

Roman period

The Roman occupation of Britain began in 43 AD but did not affect Cumbria for a further forty years; occupation then continued until 383 AD, a period of domination lasting more than three hundred years. The strategic value of Cumbria was as part of a line of defence against both the Picts in Scotland and, paradoxically, the so-called 'Scots' in Ireland. Of course the most famous of all defensive lines, Hadrian's Wall, was just to the north of the Lake District. Thus the Roman influence was primarily a military one but it did open up major lines of communication through the difficult mountainous terrain, with one major highway from near Kendal to the important harbour at Ravenglass on the west coast, and another over High Street (the mountain range being named after the old Roman road). The Windermere valley was an important Roman region, with a fort for some five hundred soldiers built around 100 AD at Galava at the head of the lake. The site of the Roman fort is still visible today at Borrans Field in Ambleside. Another important Roman fort can be seen just outside the Windermere catchment on Hardknott Pass. In terms of their direct impact on the local environment, the Romans largely left the native Cumbrians (more correctly referred to as the native Celts or Britons*) to their own devices. No doubt some interbreeding with the Roman troops (drawn from the frontier provinces of the Roman Empire) occurred and other northern Celts in close contact with the occupying forces were probably 'romanised' to some degree. The Romans introduced improved iron implements to the area, enabling the native Celts to extend the area of agricultural land. Several attempts (some successful) were made to overthrow Hadrian's Wall and in 383 AD most of the Roman troops were withdrawn from Britain, leaving the local population to fend for itself. With increasing raids on Cumbria from the Picts and the Scots, Britain slipped into the Dark Ages.

*[Cumbria is derived from Welsh *Cymru* (= Wales). The Celtic Britons living in North Wales, Cumbria and south-west Scotland up to Strathclyde were part of the *Cymry* (= people of Wales), speaking a 'Welsh' language. The influence of Welsh princes and kings in Cumbria faded out after the 6th century AD].

Anglian influences

From the middle of the 6th century AD the Anglians, originating from the north German plain, began to settle in lowland England. At this time Cumbria was still a Celtic stronghold with close cultural links with southern Scotland, north Wales and Cornwall. The Anglians, essentially from an agricultural culture, brought with them a new implement, an ox-drawn plough that could cut the sod and also plough a deep furrow. This enabled a further extension of agriculture to areas that hitherto were too heavy for the existing implements to work and, during the next two centuries, the Anglian culture gradually extended into Cumbria. At the same time, the native Celts probably continued to herd their sheep and produce their crops in 'traditional' ways until the next major influence – the so-called Viking invasion.

Norse-Irish colonisation

The popular perception of Viking influences on Britain is of marauding bands of Danes and Norwegians sailing across the North Sea in longboats and wreaking havoc on the eastern coastal communities. Curiously, the colonisation of Cumbria was from the *west*. Having worked (some might say raped and pillaged) their way around the north and west coasts of Scotland, the Norse invaders had colonised Ireland and the Isle of Man by the 9th century AD. By this time they were probably Norse-Irish rather than true Scandinavians and it was from this direction that they eventually ended up in Cumbria. Their sculpture has definite Celtic affinities and their place names contain elements from the Gaelic language. These settlers were pastoral people looking for good land to graze sheep but, as immigrants, they may have had to develop the more marginal land in the first instance. 'Thwaite' derives from the Scandinavian name for a clearing in the forest – check a map for the number of 'thwaites' in the Windermere catchment. In addition to sheep (and cattle), the Norse-Irish also brought pigs, which thrive in woodlands. No doubt these activities would have contributed to a reduced regeneration of the trees and eventual conversion to grazing land. Swindale and Grizedale are names associated with the keeping of pigs. By the 10th century, despite all this Scandinavian influence, Cumbria was politically in the hands of Scotland. What then followed was a major Norman-French influence on this part of the British Isles.

Norman conquest

The English defeat at the battle of Hastings in 1066 AD had no immediate impact on the Lake District which, at the time, was some sort of 'no-man's land' between England and Scotland. Indeed, in the great Domesday inventory of newly acquired Norman territory, the Lake District is not mentioned. However, by the end of the 11th century the Norman dynasty had claimed much of the territory. The Normans were deeply religious and brought with them feudalism and monasticism. Furness Abbey was established in 1127 AD, initially as a Benedictine foundation, but within twenty years it had become a Cistercian house. The Cistercians were great agriculturists and did much to improve agricultural practices around the periphery of the Lake District in the 12th century. During the 12th and 13th centuries, some of these large religious establishments made considerable agricultural inroads into the valleys of the Lake District proper, including Windermere. Furness Abbey owned the western half of the Windermere catchment and lost little time in making the fells productive. The Abbey established a major farm at Hawkshead (Haukr's shieling) and used the surrounding hillsides for sheep pasture. Inevitably, this meant a continuation of deforestation to create new grazing as the religious houses became wealthy from the profits of the wool industry. The market towns of Ulverston and Kendal began their development at this time, in response to this new wool-based economy in the region. At the same time the monks began the process of making charcoal, to create a fuel with sufficient heat and chemical reaction for smelting iron. Iron ore was brought into the Windermere catchment from the Furness area on packhorses (possibly also using boat transport on the lake) and small iron-smelting sites or 'bloomeries' were established. The production of charcoal generally used the underwood coppice and, in this respect, contributed to the sustainable management of woodlands. In summary therefore, the 12th and 13th centuries witnessed extensive clearance of some of the upland areas for sheep rearing, greater woodland management for charcoal production, and drainage in the valley floors as grain production was increased to help feed the expanding agricultural communities in the catchment.

During this period, the Kingdom of Scotland regarded Cumbria as lost territory and by the 14th century, following the English defeat at Bannockburn, the Scots

began to increase their raids across the border. Indeed, in 1322 they pushed as far south as Lancaster before they decided to retreat. The remains of 'pele towers' in the Lake District, built as defensive refuges against these raiding parties, bear testimony to this period of unrest.

A pele tower attached to Burneside Hall, near Kendal.

In reality, it is unlikely that these raids had much impact on the developing agricultural industry within the valleys, because easier 'pickings' could be found in the Eden valley and the west Cumbrian coastal plain. Nevertheless, the overall effect must have been a downturn in the economy of the area during the 14th century, before the raids ended in the 15th century.

Further agricultural and industrial development

The 16th century saw the start of a period of limited enclosure of the fells of the Windermere catchment, a process that was accelerated following the dissolution of Furness Abbey in 1537. The wool industry continued to flourish but wool was sent to Kendal and Ulverston rather than to the Abbey. If not used for sheep (hardy animals that may have been ancestors of the present-day Herdwicks), the thin acid soils were used for the cultivation of oats and barley, both grains for making bread and barley also for brewing. Farm equipment was still primitive but by the 17th century carts were replacing packhorses for agricultural transport. About this time there was also an important change in the way buildings were constructed, with a shift from timber to stone as the primary construction material. This has made a great contribution to the character of today's man-made environment in the Windermere catchment, with a superb legacy of 17th century houses and barns such as those at Troutbeck.

At the same time, the mineral wealth (particularly lead and copper) of the Lakeland fells was arousing interest. Some of the earliest mine-workings date back to the 16th century (e.g. in the Newlands Valley) but the period of greatest prosperity and mineral output was in the latter half of the 19th century. The opportunities for bulk transport, using the growing railway network (see below), did much to promote both the mining and tourist industries in the area.

With respect to mining, the Windermere catchment did not feature as prominently as other areas, although copper was mined at Greenburn in the head of Little Langdale (the sediments of Elterwater show clear evidence of copper contamination). However, the impact of mining in Coniston, Borrowdale, and on the Skiddaw Slates to the north, continued to influence the coppice management policy of the Windermere woodland resource, with a growing demand for charcoal required for smelting. Copper-mining in the Coniston catchment, following a temporary period of closure in the 18th century, continued until the late 19th century and the largest lead-mine in England at Greenside, in the Ullswater catchment, was finally closed in 1962. Other mines in the region were also active (some up to the 20th century) but these are now closed, their overgrown spoil-heaps still bearing testimony to this earlier industry. However, even after the heyday of the Cumbrian mining industry, charcoal was still required for the manufacture of gunpowder and several mills were located in the Windermere catchment. In the 18th century, charcoal boats were a regular feature on Windermere and Coniston Water – servicing the gunpowder mills and also a few bloomeries that were still manufacturing wrought iron. The bloomeries were finally replaced in the early 18th century by the development of blast furnaces (producing cast iron) in the growing industrial areas of England. Gunpowder was manufactured in the Windermere catchment well into the 20th century, with important sites at Elterwater, Black Beck and Low Wood on the River Leven.

A positive effort was made to reforest parts of the Windermere catchment in the late 18th century. Initially this was the work of a major landowner, Mr John Curwen of Belle Isle, who replanted a large area of the western shore of Windermere with a range of tree species, including the non-native larch (much to the chagrin of the poet, William Wordsworth). Chapter 3 summarises current land use within the Windermere catchment and modern forestry activities.

Having emphasised the importance of the mining industry, this section would be incomplete without reference to quarrying for slate. Chapter 2 deals with the geological origin of the slate-beds in Cumbria. For centuries they have been exploited for roofing material and, since the 1960s, as architectural stone (often polished) for cladding and flooring. In the Windermere catchment the main centres of activity are at Elterwater, Skelwith Bridge and Kirkstone. The quarrying and stone-cutting processes have added fine rock-dust to the sediment loads entering Windermere via the River Brathay and Stock Ghyll.

The final piece in the agricultural jigsaw puzzle (almost literally) occurred during the 18th and 19th centuries, when there was a major move from arable farming to livestock production in the valleys. Local stone was used to create dry-stone walls for retaining the grazing animals and these walls are still very much in evidence today, giving the valley bottoms and sides of the Lake District their distinctive character. The enclosures in the Langdales are particularly good examples, the development of which has been studied by the National Trust – indeed, work by the Trust shows that some of the boundaries and enclosures pre-date the 18th century. During the period of enclosure, farmers also experimented with the use of lime and basic slag for 'sweetening' the pastures, a forerunner of the modern practice of using artificial fertilisers.

A landscape of stone walls enclosing small fields in Mickleden (upper Langdale).

Development of tourism

Tourism in the Lake District really began towards the end of the 18th century, following the publication of a series of descriptive accounts of the scenery. However, it was no small undertaking to travel long distances by coach and horse and the number of visitors must have been small. In the 19th century it became fashionable for the wealthy to build large country houses. The owners were mainly industrialists from Lancashire, especially Manchester, and ship-owners from Liverpool, and they built expensive houses in a variety of different styles (Jacobean, Georgian and 19th century pseudo-Gothic – Wray Castle on the shores of Windermere being, perhaps, the most grotesque example in Romanesque style (p. 3)). Many of these large houses, with their extensive landscaped gardens and grounds, have now been converted into some of the most prestigious hotels in the region. However, access to the Lake District only became available to the wider public after 1847, when the railway line to Windermere was opened. Originally it was planned that the railway would end at Ambleside, at the head of the lake, but this plan was dropped on the grounds that there would not be enough traffic to justify the additional expenditure. A railway line to Lakeside was also opened in 1869 and the visitor had the pleasure of an early, integrated transport network, linked by two steamers on the lake (the Furness Railway pioneered the idea of 'runabout' tickets in the 1890s). William Wordsworth had a vision of the Lake District as "a sort of national property in which every man has a right and an interest who has an eye to perceive and a heart to enjoy". Paradoxically, he condemned the building of the Oxenholme to Windermere railway line and warned against the impact of mass tourism. In the 20th century, the increased use of private motorcars and development of the motorway system made it inevitable that mass tourism would become an important part of the region's economy.

Direct human impacts on the lake

So far, we have briefly examined how humans have *indirectly* affected Windermere, primarily through changes in land use within the catchment. However, in several other ways, human activities have *directly* affected the lake, many of which are evident at the present time.

Agricultural runoff

The earlier part of this chapter deals with changing agricultural practices, particularly the growing dominance of sheep rearing and the associated deforestation. Agriculture has directly affected waterbodies in the Windermere catchment, largely as the result of material runoff. An analysis of the nutrient chemistry of Windermere over the last fifty years reveals increasing levels of nitrate in both basins of the lake. This is undoubtedly influenced by the growing deposition of nitrogen from the atmosphere (see below) but also reflects the increased use of inorganic nitrogenous fertilisers in the catchment. It is difficult, if not impossible, to retain all of the nitrogen on the land or in the vegetation (its intended target) and some inevitably finds its way into watercourses. Traditionally, nitrogen normally has not been considered to be a 'limiting' nutrient for plant growth in Windermere, where phosphorus fulfils this role (Chapter 6), but recent research reveals that nitrogen is, perhaps, more important than we originally thought in controlling the growth of plants in some fresh waters.

Another possible direct impact of agriculture is loss of soil as the result of ploughing or overgrazing. Within the Windermere catchment there is clear evidence of accelerated accumulation of soil in the sediments of Blelham Tarn (p. 23) during the last thirty years, and this seems to correlate with an increase in the density of livestock (primarily sheep) within that part of the catchment. However, other changes in agricultural practices associated with ploughing and re-seeding pastures could also have influenced soil/sediment accumulation in the tarn. On the higher fells there is evidence of contemporary soil and slope instability. Heavy grazing has almost certainly contributed to the problem and any future change in the frequency of high rainfall events (see Chapter 9 for information on climate change) could exacerbate the situation. In some areas there is also local erosion of footpaths.

Sheep are prone to parasitic infestations on their skin and fleece. Of particular concern is the sheep mite, which can cause a serious, ulcerating condition of the skin known as sheep scab. To prevent this occurring, sheep have to be dipped in insecticide at regular intervals. Until recently organophosphorus compounds were used for this purpose, but health concerns for the safety of the farmers carrying out this dipping operation have led to replacement of the insecticides based on organophosphorus, by synthetic pyrethroids. These are natural compounds derived from plants of the pyrethrum family and synthetic versions are widely used as horticultural insecticides. Undoubtedly they are more 'user-friendly' and are effective against sheep scab. However, they are particularly toxic to aquatic invertebrates and, when they find their way into watercourses, can cause serious pollution incidents, even at concentrations as low as a few parts per billion. Unfortunately, several such cases have occurred during recent years (some in the Windermere catchment), largely the result of careless or illegal disposal of spent sheep dip. In some instances, however, the runoff from the wet fleece of recently dipped animals has been known to kill most of the stream invertebrates for several hundreds of metres downstream of a known crossing-point used by sheep. When one considers that the fleece of a sheep can hold something like two litres of sheep dip it is not surprising that such incidents still occur. Curiously, young fish are not normally affected by the pyrethroid but their food organisms are. Crustaceans are particularly vulnerable to this form of poisoning, posing a threat to the native

Atlantic stream or white-clawed crayfish *Austropotamobius pallipes* that lives in the area. This crayfish is already the focus of conservation activity because the Lake District is currently free from the introduced American signal crayfish *Pacifastacus leniusculus*, which may carry with it a fungal infection to which the native crayfish is completely vulnerable.

The native crayfish of Britain and Ireland is threatened by plague fungus. Crayfish occur in only a few streams on the catchment of Windermere but they are relatively common in catchments to the east, where the water is more calcareous.

Sheep-dipping continues to be a problem, the solution to which (at least in the short term) lies in better communication between environmental managers and the farming community. The Environment Agency has already made good progress in raising awareness of the problem, which ought to result in a reduction in the number and severity of such pollution incidents.

Atmospheric pollution

Given the rural nature of the Lake District, it seems strange to be considering atmospheric pollution as one of the direct impacts of man. However, we now know that the transport of atmospheric pollutants is global; for example, PCBs (polychlorinated biphenyls) – perfect examples of man-made pollutants – can be detected in the polar regions, thousands of miles away from PCB manufacture or usage. Thus there is no reason to believe that the English Lake District will not be affected by a variety of pollutants carried in the atmosphere.

Perhaps the most obvious case is that of 'acid rain'. Rainwater is naturally acidic, but the impact of atmospheric pollutants can increase the degree of acidity quite markedly. The principal culprits are sulphur dioxide (produced mainly from burning coal) and oxides of nitrogen, which are converted in the atmosphere to sulphuric and nitric acid, respectively. Oxides of nitrogen are formed when petroleum is burned but may also be produced by certain intensive agricultural practices. Studies of sediments from the beds of several upland tarns in the Lake District show quite conclusively that acid rain, from industrial pollution further south, has been a problem in this area for almost two hundred years. The worst affected waterbodies are those lying on the Borrowdale Volcanic rocks of the central dome of the Lake District, and especially on the granitic intrusion in Eskdale

(Chapter 2), where the soils and rocks have a relatively poor buffering capacity. Windermere, lying mainly on Silurian slates of the Windermere Supergroup, has not shown evidence of severe acidification from atmospheric deposition. Although, over the last two centuries, some of the upland tarns have become ten times more acid than they ought to be, recent scientific evidence (both chemical and biological) indicates that they are now beginning to recover as we begin to control sulphur emissions from industry. However, it is unlikely that the endpoints for such recovery will be the same as their starting points, before the industrial revolution, because the world we now live in has significantly more 'active' nitrogen in its atmosphere. Thus nitric acid continues to be an atmospheric pollution problem. In addition to its direct effects on the acidification of tarns and lakes, nitric acid (which is a nitrate) is also a form of plant fertiliser and contributes to the problem of enrichment, or eutrophication. This issue is dealt with in more detail in Chapter 6.

An even more specific example of the long-distance transport of atmospheric pollution is that of Chernobyl, the Russian nuclear-powered reactor that exploded on the 26th of April 1986. During the next few weeks, radioactive contamination (primarily caesium[137]) spread across Western Europe and was deposited in the Lake District, on two separate occasions, in early May. The most intense deposition occurred in rainfall on the western fells, ironically those closest to the Sellafield nuclear-power station. Subsequent studies of the behaviour of this contamination showed that its accumulation in the plants and animals of the contaminated area is largely controlled by the amount of clay minerals in the soils. In the fells of west Cumbria the soils are very organic (i.e. they contain plant remains as peat), with few clay minerals which can 'lock up' the radioactive caesium by tightly binding caesium to the particles of clay. Consequently the contamination has continued to cycle between the vegetation, animals such as grazing sheep, the organic soils, and back into the vegetation. It is largely for this reason that problems of contaminated lamb from the area have persisted for as long as they have. Similar processes also occur in lakes of the area and the fish from lakes with catchments dominated by organic soils have contained more radioactive caesium than fish from other lakes, like Windermere, where the moderate amount of clay minerals undoubtedly protected the fish populations to some extent from this unexpected source of contamination. However, recent scientific evidence suggests that binding of radiocaesium to clay minerals is reversible and, therefore, the time taken to complete recovery will be much longer than was originally anticipated. The decline in contamination is being carefully monitored and, fortunately, the incident is not known to have posed a significant threat to human health in the area. Nevertheless, the disaster is a sobering reminder of man's potential to contaminate large areas of the planet's surface for extensive periods of time.

Abstraction of water

Some of the large Cumbrian lakes comprise a vital water resource for areas remote from the Lake District. Much of the infrastructure was developed in the late 19th and early 20th centuries and this now consists of a series of rivers and lakes (some interconnected) supplying water to the Carlisle region, the West Cumbrian coast, the Furness area and industrial Lancashire (particularly the Manchester area). Windermere forms part of this infrastructure, where water is abstracted from the North Basin of the lake at Calgarth and pumped to the main treatment plant at Watchgate, near Kendal.

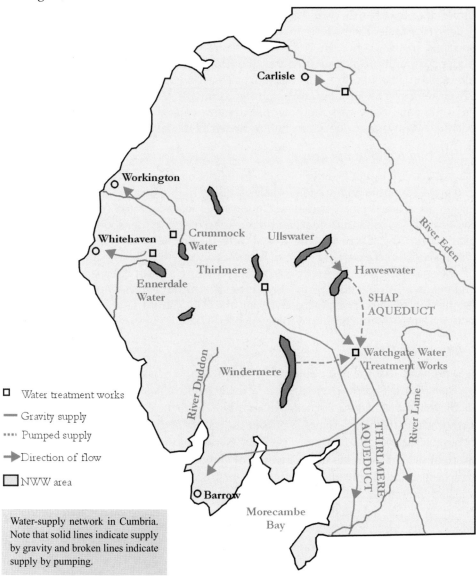

Water-supply network in Cumbria. Note that solid lines indicate supply by gravity and broken lines indicate supply by pumping.

From Watchgate the treated water is then distributed, via the main aqueducts, to most of South Cumbria and industrial Lancashire. Haweswater and Thirlmere are the most important water resources, but Windermere is a crucial source providing a contingency supply during prolonged periods of dry weather. The abstraction licence for Windermere is two hundred and five million litres per day, but abstraction is not permitted if flows to the River Leven are less than two hundred and seventy-two million litres per day during May to September, or one hundred and thirty-six million litres per day during October to April.

During severe drought conditions, the water in Windermere assumes increasing importance and North West Water (now United Utilities) may apply for drought orders to enable abstraction to continue when river-flows are less than those specified in the licence. In 1995, water abstraction from the lake was permitted under a drought order provided that the flow to the River Leven exceeded forty-five million litres per day. This figure was considered to be the minimum required to ensure survival of migratory salmonids in the River Leven. The other key environmental issue was the potential damage caused by dredging (to create an adequate clearance for boats in shallow areas) as the lake-level was lowered.

Extraction of sand and gravel

Glacial activity in the Windermere catchment (Chapter 2) has left significant sand and gravel deposits on the bed of the lake, partly in the form of lateral moraines but largely as submerged river deltas. The resource was exploited commercially until the early 1970s, using fifty-foot sand-barges as a platform for scooping the sand and gravel from the lakebed using a pole and derrick assembly – later techniques employed a direct pumping system. A major concern was the impact of this activity on the spawning sites of Arctic charr which require a clean open gravel, and were endangered by siltation from the 'fines' produced by the operation. Indeed, permission for any dredging activity on the lake should take into consideration potential impacts on charr spawning sites (p. 47).

Commercial fisheries

It is probable that the fish populations of Windermere have always been exploited by man, but the earliest reference to a fishery on the lake goes back to the early medieval period, when Furness Abbey owned much of the land. One boat was authorised to fish using twenty nets but the nature of these nets and the method of fishing is not known. In later periods, seine netting (originally referred to as draught netting) was the usual method of choice and by the 16th century the lake had been divided into distinct sections, or 'cubbles', for the purposes of fishery legislation and control. The nets were used to catch Arctic charr, trout, pike and perch. In addition, baited hooks on 'long lines' were used to catch pike, perch and eels. It is also possible that an early form of gill-netting (using 'case nets') was used for a period but this was banned in the late 18th century. It is difficult to estimate the size of the catches but by the middle of the 19th century there was evidence of overfishing of the charr populations. The charr were particularly valuable and were transported as far south as London, usually in the form of potted charr. By the 18th and 19th centuries, pots were specifically made for this purpose and, today, decorated Windermere charr pots are collector's items. The last commercial seine-net fishery on Windermere was closed in 1921.

In the early 19th century a rod-and-line fishery developed for charr. This was a new approach using several hooks simultaneously and one form of this technique, the plumb line, is still used today in a semi-commercial fishery that provides charr for local consumption. Fishing from a rowing boat, the charr fisherman uses a large pole from each side of the boat, with a plumb line attached to a heavy lead weight. Sidelines are attached at regular intervals from the main plumb line and a metal spinner is used as a lure at the end of each sideline. The metal baits are hand-made, often from precious metals, and are highly polished to attract the fish. The success of this method is something of a paradox because the fish that are caught are usually feeding on zooplankton (Chapter 4), yet the baits most probably represent small fish.

Metal lures used for catching Arctic charr in Windermere.

During the Second World War an exploratory fishery was developed to catch perch, which were than canned in tomato sauce and sold as 'perchines', a substitute for sardines during a time of austerity. The fish were caught in unbaited traps during their spawning season and some ninety tonnes of perch were removed from Windermere between 1941 and 1947. Similar fisheries were attempted in other lakes but these were far less successful and none lasted for more than two or three years.

During the Second World War, perch from Windermere were caught in unbaited traps (*left*) and sent by rail overnight to a factory in Leeds, where they were canned in Yorkshire relish and tomato ketchup to make them more palatable. The tins (*below*) were labelled as 'Perchines – Lakeland Perch, Britain's most lovely and tasty fresh water fish'. They were cheap to buy and required only a few wartime food-ration coupons.

After the war an extensive programme of trapping perch continued as part of ongoing scientific studies on various aspects of the population dynamics of perch in the lake. These include measurements of numbers, size, sex and growth rates, the ages of fish (some perch live for more than 15 years) and the annual recruitment of young fish into the population. The accmulation of a large amount of data over many decades is crucial for understanding the science of fisheries and their management (both freshwater and marine). Obtaining such information for perch, pike (an important predator) and charr has continued since the 1940s, although at much reduced levels in recent years for perch and pike.

For monitoring perch, five traps are currently set at each of four sites, one in the North Basin and three in the South Basin. This is done in April to June each year.

Six commercial netting licences to catch salmon and sea trout in the estuary of the River Leven have been operational for at least fifteen years and eel traps, capturing silver eels during their downstream autumn migration to the sea, have operated in the past on the River Leven. In addition, occasional licences have been granted for fyke-netting in Windermere. Fyke nets are fixed to the bed of the lake and are used as a form of trap, selectively to catch eels. Unlike all other freshwater fish populations, eels comprise a single population across Europe, spawning collectively in the Sargasso Sea, and there is now serious concern about declining eel stocks in most European countries.

With the exception of the semi-commercial charr fishery on Windermere, present-day fishing activities on the lake are largely restricted to angling for pleasure. This includes trout fishing by bait or fly, pike angling and coarse fishing. With a growing roach population in the lake (Chapter 9), it is possible that coarse fishing will assume increasing importance in the future.

Boat traffic

The early industrial traffic on the lake (see above) led to a right of navigation and this, in turn, led to the introduction of navigation rules. The bye-law-making provision of the Countryside Act of 1968 then opened the way for further controls on boat speed and behaviour on the lake. No-one who now visits Windermere can fail to notice the large number of pleasure craft on the lake.

Pleasure craft moored in a sheltered bay.

On Windermere, pleasure craft include canoes, rowing boats, sailing craft and, of course, motor-powered vessels. The latter range in size from the modern, one-person jet-ski to the large passenger steamers that ply between Ambleside, Bowness-on-Windermere and Lakeside. All motor-powered vessels on the lake have to be registered with the Lake District National Park Authority and, at the time of writing, approximately six and a half thousand vessels are registered each year and there are over one thousand moorings and six hundred boathouses, slip-ways and jetties on the lake. This gives some impression of the popularity of Windermere as a boating venue! It has been almost inevitable that this competition for the resource has led to conflict and plans are now in place to stop fast power boating and water skiing (see below).

However, it is highly probable that boats have been used on Windermere since humans first settled in the area. For example, a local, polished Neolithic stone axe has been recovered in west Cumbria from a site that also revealed the remains of a dugout canoe. We have also seen how the monks of Furness Abbey used boats on Windermere for transporting iron ore and wool during the 12th and 13th centuries and how this tradition was continued into the 19th century with steam transport for shipping coal, charcoal and slate. Since the decline of this traffic the lake has been used primarily for pleasure.

At one time or another most visitors to Windermere will have crossed the lake by means of the passenger and car ferry that runs between Ferry Nab and The Ferry House – it may surprise some readers to learn that a ferry crossing at this point has been in existence for at least five hundred years. Originally powered by oars and human sweat, the ferry was an extremely important route for the wool trade, linking Hawshead to the market town of Kendal.

Undoubtedly the ferry's most tragic moment occurred in 1635, when all forty-seven members of a wedding party were drowned as the ferry sank in a gale. The victims are buried in a mass grave at St. Martins Church, Bowness-on-Windermere. Oars were eventually replaced by steam power, which in turn gave way to the modern, diesel-engined ferry we see today. It operates on cables that are anchored on each side of the lake.

One very specific form of boat traffic, the flying boat, made its appearance on the lake during the years of the Second World War. A factory building Sunderland flying boats was established at White Cross Bay, on the east shore of the North Basin of Windermere, and became an important contribution to the war effort. Many of these planes ended up on civilian routes during the post-war years and a handful, in the tender care of flying boat enthusiasts, are still operational. There are apocryphal stories of scuttled Sunderland flying boats lying on the bed of Windermere but, to the author's knowledge, no such wreck has been located.

The current passenger and car ferry on Windermere. Powered by diesel engines, the ferry pulls itselfs across the lake on two very long steel cables, one on each side. Each cable is wound round a large central wheel.

If you have an opportunity, it is worth spending a few moments looking at the present-day boats on Windermere, because some of these reflect the boating history of the lake. The most graceful of the passenger steamers is undoubtedly the *Tern*. Built in 1891, originally as a steamboat but now powered by diesel, the *Tern* still displays elegance from its Victorian/Edwardian origins. A collection of steam launches from the same era is housed at the Bowness Steam Boat Museum; most of these boats are still operational and can be seen on the lake during various regattas.

Finally, Windermere has its very own sailing yacht, the Windermere Class. These 17-foot, keeled sailing boats were first introduced in 1904 and are still built today (in very limited numbers). They regularly race from the Royal Windermere Yacht Club during the summer months and, in good wind, these yachts make a spectacular and unique sight on the lake.

Above: The *Tern*, one of three pleasure steamers that travel up and down the lake, calling at Lakeside, Bowness-on-Windermere and Ambleside. *Below:* Yachts of the Windermere Class. Built locally, these 17-foot racing yachts have deep keels filled with lead, to counter-balance the large area of the two sails.

The 10 mph speed limit

No account of the boating issues relating to Windermere can be complete without a brief summary of a successful move to apply a 10 mph speed limit to the lake. Originating from boating 'incidents' on the lake and their potential consequences for health and safety, together with a call for greater tranquillity in an area of great natural beauty, in 1992 the Lake District National Park Authority (LDNPA) put forward proposals to the Home Office to restrict the speed limit of boats on Windermere. The proposal was largely supported by conservation organisations and the South Lakeland District Council but opposed by the power-boating and water-skiing fraternity (and a significant section of the local business community) who, hitherto, had relatively unrestricted use of the lake for their sport. The Home Secretary ordered a public inquiry to consider all the evidence because of the significant numbers of objections to the proposed bye-law. The initial decision by the LDNPA, the subsequent inquiry and its outcome have generated a great deal of controversy and lobbying.

The inquiry began in the summer of 1994 and many interested organisations and individuals gave evidence, both for and against the proposed speed limit. It took some eighteen months for the Inspector to prepare and deliver his report, during which time the governmental responsibility for a final decision had been transferred to the then Department of the Environment. The Inspector's report was presented to the Secretary of State for the Environment in February 1996, with an overall recommendation that the speed limit bye-law should be confirmed. Having considered the Inquiry Report and the Inspector's recommendation, the then Secretary of State took a different view and, in August 1996, wrote to the LDNPA refusing to confirm the bye-laws (on the grounds that, for many years, Windermere had been an important power-boating venue and on which there was a public right of navigation) whilst encouraging both sides to explore ways in which they might integrate activities on the lake more effectively.

The LDNPA then took the decision to seek leave to apply for a Judicial Review of the Secretary of State's decision, and this was granted in November 1996. However, a general election intervened and the new, incoming government decided not to support the decision by the former government but to undertake a review of the findings of the original inquiry. Following a period of further, written consultation with all participants, the new Secretary of State for the Environment, Regions and Transport confirmed the speed limit bye-laws and these were enacted, with an enforcement date of March 2005. The local community is still divided on the 'pros' and 'cons' of the issues.

Waste disposal

In the UK we have used most of our fresh waters as 'receiving' waters for treated sewage effluent and Windermere is no exception. However, until halfway through the 20th century, the disposal of waste water within the catchment was uncoordinated and dispersed. With a growing residential population and an influx of tourists into the area, centralised and improved forms of treating waste water have been developed and this has undoubtedly prevented many potential, local health hazards within the catchment. Nevertheless, one consequence of this progress has been the increased reliance on Windermere as a diluting receptacle for treated waste waters. This has various implications for the state of health of the lake, one of which (enrichment by plant nutrients) is dealt with in the next chapter.

However, three parts of the shoreline around Windermere are now designated as bathing-water beaches under the EC Bathing Water Directive. These are at Miller Ground in the North Basin, and at the YMCA Lakeside and at Fell Foot in the South Basin. Indeed, Windermere is one of the most important UK inland waters to be designated under the Directive. Clearly, the dual use of the waterbody for waste-water disposal and for bathing requires careful management and the 'designated' status ensures that appropriate microbiological monitoring is routinely undertaken at all three sites. A particular issue in this respect is the influence of storm water on the sewerage system, which has the potential to cause local pollution problems, and North West Water is addressing some of the more serious discharges from combined sewer overflows under the Asset Management Plan (AMP 3, 2003 to 2005), as agreed between the company and the Environment Agency.

The winter concentrations of dissolved phosphorus in the water of the South Basin gradually increased to between fifteen and twenty times the background levels measured during the 1940s and 1950s (about 2 micrograms per litre), reaching a peak of about forty micrograms per litre in 1991. This single change in water chemistry has probably had more impact on the biology of the lake than the combined effect of all the other human influences described in the previous chapter.

Algal production

From our knowledge of the natural succession of algal species in Windermere (Chapter 4), it ought not to surprise us that this man-made enrichment of the lake from secondarily treated sewage effluents has had a major impact on algal productivity. One of the most visible effects has been the colonisation of the shoreline rocks, particularly around the South Basin, by the so-called 'blanket weed' *Cladophora glomerata*. Blanket weeds are filamentous green algae that use large stones and rocks in shallow water as an anchor. However, they obtain all their nutrients directly from the water. By the early 1990s, blanket weed dominated the edges of the lake, thereby creating an unsightly and slippery marginal zone for those using the lake. More importantly, it completely altered the natural habitat for the young trout living around the margins of Windermere (Chapter 4).

Blanket weed on a rocky shore.

Of even greater importance was the impact of this nutrient enrichment on the planktonic algae. The effect on diatoms (the dominant algae during the early part of the season) has not been particularly marked, because they normally run out of silica before they have used up all the phosphorus. However, this has an important 'knock-on' effect on subsequent blooms of algae because the latter can then use the phosphorus left behind by the diatoms and, as a consequence, the greatest impact of nutrient enrichment is on the later summer and autumn blooms (primarily green and blue-green algae). Between 1964 and 1991 there was a progressive increase in the summer peak of algal production (measured in terms of the maximum concentration of chlorophyll in the water). However, there also were very marked year-to-year variations in the magnitude of these

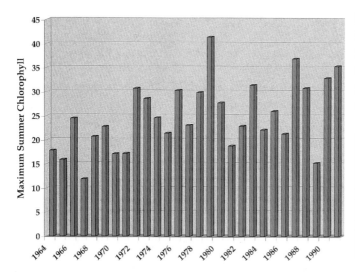

blooms, emphasising the additional and important effects that weather patterns have on the final crop of algae.

Peak summer chlorophyll concentrations (micrograms per litre) recorded in Windermere South Basin, from 1964 to 1991. This is a convenient way of estimating the relative amounts of algal growth each year.

In summary, the increased nutrient levels increase the window of opportunity for algal growth, but the extent to which this is exploited by the algae is still strongly weather-dependent.

During the 1980s, the blue-green alga (or cyanobacterium) *Tychonema bourrellyi* dominated the late summer crops of phytoplankton. This filamentous species grows particularly well when the lake is thermally stratified (Chapter 3) and when the upper layer of water (the *epilimnion*) is well mixed by summer winds. This gentle, turbulent mixing keeps the algal filaments suspended in the water column, where they thrive on the readily available nutrients in the lake. However, unlike many planktonic algae, *T. bourrellyi* does not have any specialist adaptations (such as gas vacuoles or oil droplets) to maintain its buoyancy in the water. As a consequence, during periods of calm weather the filaments begin to sink from the upper layers of the lake into the underlying deeper, colder water (the *hypolimnion*). Once the algal cells have sunk beneath the thermocline there is no route back to the sunlit surface waters until the lake completely mixes during the autumn 'overturn'.

So for the rest of the growing season these cells are destined to remain in the deep water. Not only is this water cold, it is also dark, partly because the algal cells remaining in the upper layers block out much of the light from above and also because sunlight is readily absorbed by fresh water.

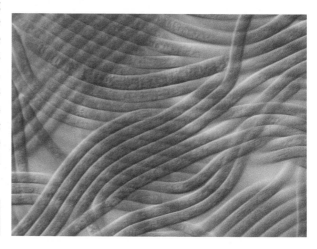

Filaments of the blue-green alga *Tychonema bourrellyi*.

Because the underwater light intensity decreases rapidly with depth, the alga responds just like any other plant removed from its source of light and many of the *T. bourrellyi* filaments in the hypolimnion die and decompose. We have seen from Chapter 4 that microbial decomposition is a key factor in recycling the constituent components of dead organic matter back into the food web, but the processes use up oxygen and so reduce the concentration of dissolved oxygen in the deeper parts of the lake. Some of the *T. bourrellyi* cells, however, are remarkably resistant to microbial decomposition and survive during the winter months in the surface sediments of the lake. These cells form the inoculum for the next season's growth and the whole cycle is then repeated.

The Windermere charr

As we have seen above, the effect of increased algal productivity during the summer months in Windermere, in response to elevated phosphorus levels, is a decrease in the dissolved oxygen concentration of the deeper parts of the lake. To illustrate the progression of this particular problem, at the end of the summer in 1968 the dissolved oxygen concentrations in the deepest part of the South Basin (40 metres) dropped to just below fifty percent of air-saturation values for a period of four weeks. Twenty years later, in 1988, there was *no measurable oxygen* in exactly the same part of the lake and oxygen concentrations remained critically low for a period of two months! As explained in Chapter 4 the deeper, colder parts of Windermere are important for the survival of Arctic charr during the summer months, yet these areas of the lake lost much of their oxygen, particularly during the 1980s and early 1990s. Under such conditions the fish are forced to occupy the shallower, warmer parts of the lake if they are to avoid direct asphyxiation. Moreover, the increased annual deposition of decaying algal cells has the potential to silt up areas of gravel on the bed of the lake, and Arctic charr are the only fish in Windermere that spawn in the gravel. Thus the impacts of increased algal productivity within the lake are likely to be most severe on the charr, the species of fish that is also of greatest conservation interest.

By the early 1990s it was becoming increasingly obvious that the charr populations were in decline, particularly in the South Basin of the lake. An echo-sounding transect across each basin, on the same day in March 1990, reveals a dearth of pelagic fish in the South Basin when compared with the North Basin (p. 90). Unfortunately, echo-sounding cannot directly identify the species of fish but it does measure body size and detects shoaling behaviour. It is possible, therefore, from our knowledge of the biology of the different species of fish within the lake, to make reasonable inferences regarding the species identity for most echoes. This indicates that the majority of detected fish were Arctic charr. At the same time fishermen also reported a marked decline in their catches of charr, particularly from the South Basin of the lake, and the numbers of charr estimated from surveys made with nets near known charr spawning sites were at an all-time low. Indeed, by 1992 there was a genuine concern that we were in danger of losing the charr populations, at least from part of the lake, and from our knowledge of the genetic structure of the stocks within the lake (Chapter 4) this would effectively mean the loss of one or more unique 'gene pools'. It was at this point that a remediation strategy was drawn up, the implementation of which is described in the next chapter.

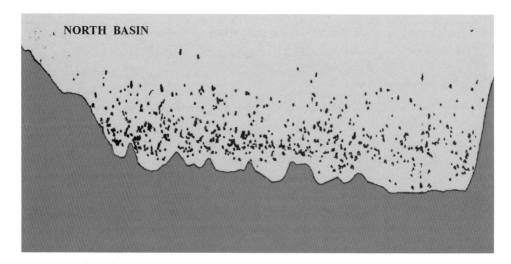

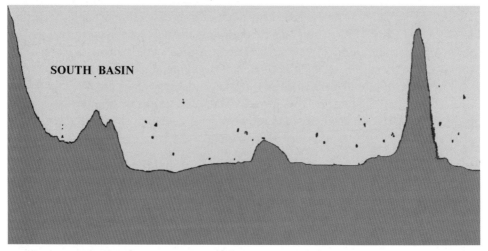

Results obtained from transects across Windermere North and South Basins on the same day in March 1990, using echo-sounding and location equipment. Individual fish or groups of fish are shown as black spots, and were far more numerous in the North Basin. The brown areas represent sediments at the bottom of the lake.

Chapter 7
Restoration of water quality in Windermere

Chapter 6 describes how general improvements to the waste-water treatment process in the Windermere catchment created a specific problem of phosphorus enrichment in the lake, particularly in the South Basin. In turn this led to excessive algal growth and a resultant loss of oxygen from the deeper, colder parts of the lake. The species most sensitive to such changes in Windermere is the Arctic charr and evidence shows that the charr numbers declined markedly during the 1980s and early 1990s. The Centre for Ecology and Hydrology (formerly the Institute of Freshwater Ecology), and the Freshwater Biological Association, collated scientific evidence of these changes from their laboratories on the west shore of the lake. The funding for this work included significant contributions from the Environment Agency (formerly the National Rivers Authority) and from North West Water. The Environment Agency is responsible for the management of the ecology and water quality within the lake and North West Water (now United Utilities) is charged with responsibility for treatment and disposal of waste waters within the catchment. However, the ultimate end-user is the general public (whether resident or visitor) who, in the main, is also the principal polluter. Thus the problem is shared by the whole community and therefore plans to attain a solution should be a combined team effort.

Phosphorus sources and sinks

Before attempting to find a solution, it is important to understand the true nature of the problem. Phosphorus entering a lake is usually in one of two basic forms: either it is attached to particles (and not easily available to aquatic plants) or it occurs in solution (as phosphate) and is readily taken up by planktonic algae and macrophytes (Chapter 4). The total annual budget (amounting to almost 20 tonnes per year) for all forms of phosphorus entering Windermere in 1991, before any major remedial work was undertaken, is shown overleaf. The overall load consists of three main components: catchment runoff, the Windermere Sewage Treatment Works (Tower Wood STW) and the Ambleside STW, with minor contributions from three smaller STWs and from rainfall. However, the nature of the phosphorus in catchment runoff is very different from that in the treated sewage effluent. Something like eighty percent of the phosphorus in the runoff is firmly bound to small particles resulting from erosional processes within the catchment and in this form it is not readily available for growth of plants (particularly algae). Much of this particulate phosphorus settles out of the water and sinks to the bed of the lake. In sharp contrast, virtually all of the phosphorus in the treated sewage effluents is in a dissolved form and is immediately available to plants. With this knowledge in mind, the key sources of nutrients are the effluents from the Ambleside and Tower Wood STWs.

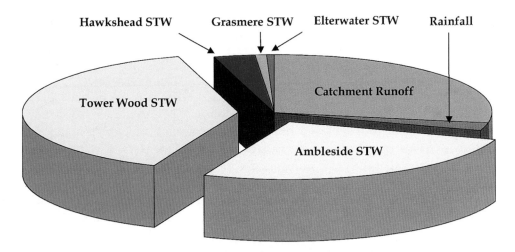

The proportions of total phosphorus entering Windermere from various sources in 1991, before remedial work was undertaken. STW represents Sewage Treatment Works. Tower Wood STW serves the Windermere and Bowness conurbation.

Having identified the most important nutrient sources, we need to understand a little about the way in which the water and the sediments interact. Much of the phosphorus that is taken up by aquatic plants (particularly the planktonic algae) will eventually find its way to the sediments of the lake as the algae (or those organisms that feed on the algae) eventually die. Thus, one inevitable consequence of increasing the phosphorus load to a lake will be an increase in the phosphorus content of the lake sediments. In a shallow lake, where the sediments are regularly re-suspended by wind-mixing, the phosphorus is re-dissolved and used again by the algae. Such recycling of nutrients is a major factor in determining the extent of algal growth in a shallow lake such as Bassenthwaite Lake. In a deep lake like Windermere, however, the re-suspension of sediments is extremely limited because most of the lake is too deep for the surface wave energy to have any impact on the bed of the lake. In effect, the sediments in water deeper than five metres will not re-suspend under normal weather conditions. For this reason there is a better prospect of improving water quality by means of nutrient control in deep lakes than there is in shallow lakes. Having said that, there *is* one mechanism that enables phosphorus to recycle from the deep sediments within a thermally stratified lake, and this occurs when the deeper water loses all of its oxygen and becomes anoxic. Under these conditions the phosphorus locked up in the more superficial sediments re-dissolves into the overlying water. However, for this phosphorus to have an important stimulatory effect on algal growth there would need to be significant mixing of the underlying deeper waters with the surface layers of the stratified lake, and the importance of such a mechanism for Windermere is not known. At the end of autumn, when the whole lake does become completely mixed again, nutrient-rich water may be brought to the surface, but by this time the shorter daylengths, lower light intensity and low temperatures are not conducive to algal growth.

In summary we have identified two key point-sources of phosphorus, and from a consideration of the depth and shape of the lake basins have reasoned that control of these nutrient sources should lead to a significant improvement in water quality in the lake. Such a case, based on the best available science, was put to North West Water (which had also co-funded much of the original research) and the Company made a commitment to install tertiary treatment to remove phosphorus from the effluents discharged from both Tower Wood and Ambleside STWs. The urgency of the conservation issues was recognised and the commitment by North West Water was made well ahead of the time when any legal requirement of the Urban Waste Water Treatment Directive (Chapter 8) came into effect.

Treatment of waste waters in the Windermere catchment

Primary treatment of sewage effluent simply refers to maceration, filtration or settlement to remove most of the solids. Secondary treatment allows sufficient time for microbial processes to metabolise much of the organic carbon and in so doing some of the larger complex molecules are broken down into smaller, simpler substances. Further stages in the waste-water treatment process are usually referred to as 'tertiary' and might include stages to remove nutrients or systems to eliminate potential pathogens (e.g. ozonisation, ultra-violet treatment, membrane filtration). The sewerage system (i.e. the network of collecting and delivery pipes) in the Windermere catchment is a dual system, designed to take waste water directly into the foul sewer but, under extremely wet conditions, to also accept excess surface runoff from roads and other paved areas. Under such conditions a proportion of the mixed surface runoff/waste water may even bypass the waste-water treatment plant and discharge directly into the receiving water with no or minimal (primary) treatment. The philosophy behind this design is that the increased dilution of the untreated effluent during periods of wet weather and high river flows minimises any adverse environmental impacts. This philosophy is perhaps acceptable when the receiving water is a river with a short residence time before discharge to a coastal zone, but not when the receiving water is a lake such as Windermere, with a long residence time. Under these circumstances the incomplete treatment of a diluted effluent and the deliberate bypass of the waste-water treatment process increases the load of carbon, nutrients and other compounds to the lake. The problem is exacerbated by the poor condition of parts of the old pipe-work in the sewerage system. This is now inherently leaky, allowing further ingress of surface water to the system.

The largest waste-water treatment works, at Tower Wood, serves about four thousand properties (resident population about 9,000) in the Bowness,

Windermere and Troutbeck area, but in the summer the population in this part of the catchment may double in size. The Tower Wood STW also takes waste water from boats on the lake, using a boat-emptying facility on the shoreline, from which it is pumped to the inlet of the STW. The original treatment works dates from 1915 but has been upgraded twice, in 1966 and again in 1992. One of the main features of the 1966 upgrade was the elimination of a settled (but otherwise untreated) storm-water overflow from the treatment works directly to the surface waters of the lake at Tower Wood. However, the present-day system still includes a large storm-water retention tank at Bowness-on-Windermere which, under conditions of high flow, discharges screened effluent into the lake. The 1992 upgrade included new primary settlement tanks, additional biological percolating filters (see below) and final settlement tanks and, crucially, the installation of a phosphate removal process.

Although it is rather complicated, a description of the waste-water treatment process at Tower Wood is given here to illustrate the application of the improved technology. The process is based upon biological treatment through slow, percolating filters which provide a suitable physical substratum and an aerobic environment for bacteria and protozoa to oxidise much of the organic carbon in the waste water to carbon dioxide. Sewage is pumped from the Glebe pumping station at Bowness-on-Windermere to the Tower Wood STW. The time taken for the sewage to reach the works is partially weather-dependent but is normally several hours. The waste water is screened to remove any large debris and the screenings are washed, macerated and pressed to remove excess water before disposal to land-fill. The screened waste water then passes slowly through a detritor – a small shallow tank with a reduced velocity of flow to allow any grit (mainly from road runoff) to settle out. From the detritor it passes to two primary settlement tanks (each of 1 million litres capacity) and remains there for some eight hours during which time the organic particles settle to the bottom of the tank where they form a sludge. The sludge is pumped to one of three silos where it is consolidated before being taken by road-tanker to Lancaster waste-water treatment works for digestion and further treatment. The final use of the treated sewage sludge is as a fertiliser on agricultural land. The settled waste water from the primary settlement tanks is then directed, via a flow-control device, to the biological percolating filters. Flows come through the centre of each of fourteen filters into the rotating arms and cascade evenly onto the filter-bed where micro-organisms break down much of the organic polluting material in the waste water. The flow from the filters is then dosed with ferric sulphate, to remove phosphate (see below), and transferred to the final settlement tanks. Solids, in the form of sludge, from the final settlement tanks are pumped to the storage silos and are processed with the primary sludge (see above). The final effluent (tertiary treated) is discharged to the South Basin of Windermere via an outfall pipe some thirty metres long and at a depth of seven metres below the surface of the lake.

Tower Wood Sewage Treatment Works on the east shore of Windermere South Basin.

The treatment process used at Tower Wood occupies a larger area of land than more modern treatment processes such as the activated sludge process, but has the advantage of minimising power consumption (much of the system is gravity-fed).

The phosphate-removal component of the above waste-water treatment process depends upon a chemical reaction with ferric ions to form insoluble ferric phosphate, although the details of the chemical reaction with different forms of phosphorus are not fully understood. Phosphorus is present in untreated waste waters in several forms (as orthophosphate, polyphosphate and organic phosphate), with an average total concentration between five and twenty milligrams per litre. Normal secondary treatment removes only one or two milligrams per litre of the total phosphorus, leaving a large excess that may be the cause of eutrophication (nutrient enrichment) in surface waters. Tertiary treatment, using ferric precipitation, has the potential to remove more than ninety percent of the remaining phosphorus, if the conditions for the chemical reaction are optimised.

The other major point-source of phosphorus in the Windermere catchment is the Ambleside STW, which operates differently from Tower Wood. Ambleside STW uses an activated-sludge treatment process that relies upon physical aeration of the primary settled effluent and involves recycling the secondary sludge, as this provides the major source of microbial activity in the system. The bacteria in the sludge are responsible for much of the metabolic activity but protozoa ensure that the sludge remains in a suitable 'floc' during the treatment process. Ferric sulphate treatment to remove phosphorus is incorporated into the system but the final process involves percolation through another type of biological filter to allow nitrifying bacteria to reduce the concentration of ammonia in the waste water. The final effluent is discharged into the River Rothay and thence to the North Basin of Windermere, but some storm-water overflow of settled but otherwise untreated effluent occurs during very wet periods. Both Ambleside and Tower Wood STWs are subject to discharge consents issued by the Environment Agency, with consent conditions for BOD (biochemical oxygen demand), suspended solids, and concentrations of ammonia, phosphorus and iron. One condition of the discharge consent demands that the concentration of total phosphorus in the final effluent does not exceed two milligrams per litre.

Recent changes in the nutrient status of the lake

Phosphorus removal was installed into the waste-water treatment processes of the Ambleside and Tower Wood STWs during 1991 and 1992. Effective operation of the ferric precipitation technology should facilitate a decrease of dissolved phosphorus levels in the lake, hopefully resulting in a reversal of some of the deleterious ecological changes outlined in the previous chapter. Because planktonic algae can rapidly deplete the concentrations of phosphate in the lake during the growing season, it is conventional to measure dissolved phosphorus concentrations during the winter months, when nutrient uptake by algae is at its lowest. Since 1991, these winter levels of dissolved phosphorus in the South Basin have declined, following introduction of tertiary phosphate stripping at Ambleside and Tower Wood STWs.

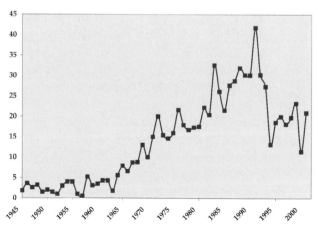

As predicted, the impact is greatest in the South Basin. This part of the lake ultimately receives effluent from both STWs and the volume of the basin (for dilution purposes) is significantly smaller than that of Windermere North Basin.

Maximum concentrations of soluble phosphorus recorded in Windermere South Basin during each winter, from 1945 to 2001.

Maximum concentrations of dissolved phosphorus in the South Basin have declined (from about 30 to 40 micrograms per litre to approximately 20 micrograms per litre) during the past decade. There is some variation in winter phosphate levels and this may be related to surface water influx to the sewerage system and the direct discharge of storm-water overflow during wet periods (Chapter 9). Thus a significant improvement in the nutrient chemistry of the lake has been achieved, but what are the consequences for algal growth, oxygen levels and the charr populations?

Algal growth in Windermere after introduction of phosphorus stripping

One of the most visible effects of phosphorus enrichment in the lake was the stimulated growth of blanket weed *Cladophora*, growing around the shores of the South Basin (Chapter 6), but there has been a substantial decline in the seasonal biomass of this large alga since phosphorus stripping was installed. Clearly, its growth in the South Basin has been reversed by the remedial treatment.

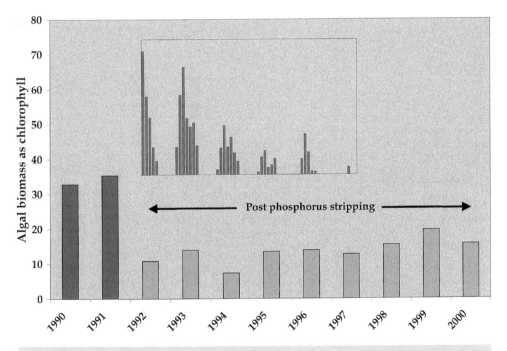

Maximum amounts of planktonic algae in Windermere South Basin, measured as chlorophyll (micrograms per litre) during the period 1990 to 2000. *Inset above:* The relative amounts of blanket weed on rocks around the shore, 1992 to 1997.

Nutrient enrichment in Windermere has the greatest effect on the late summer blooms of planktonic algae, for reasons explained in Chapter 6. Maximum concentrations of chlorophyll in the South Basin of the lake during the late summer (a measure of planktonic algal biomass) have also declined during the last decade, from about thirty micrograms per litre before 1991 to generally less than fifteen micrograms per litre in 1992 to 2000. During this latter period the historically large blooms of the problematic blue-green alga *Tychonema bourrellyi* have been conspicuously absent. These observations clearly show that the installation of phosphorus stripping at the main STWs in the Windermere catchment has had a sustained and significant effect on reducing summer growth of algae in the lake.

Oxygen concentrations in the South Basin

As predicted, the reduction in algal biomass present in the South Basin during the summer months has had a major impact and prevented the disappearance of oxygen from deep water. Between 1987 and 1991, oxygen in the deepest part of the South Basin, at forty metres depth, had almost disappeared during the autumn, when the lake was still stratified, and in 1988 this deep water became completely devoid of oxygen (anoxic). After phosphorus stripping was introduced, minimum oxygen concentrations have never dropped below one milligram per litre and in most years have been at least twice this concentration. It should be stressed that the poor water quality recorded at forty metres depth in the South Basin is a worst-case scenario – in all other parts of the lake, water quality has been and is significantly better than this.

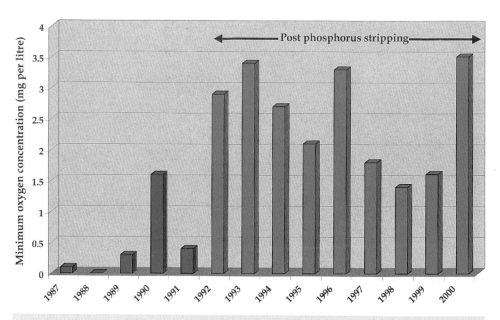

The minimum oxygen concentrations recorded in Windermere South Basin at a depth of 40 metres in late summer, from 1987 to 2000. Oxygen concentrations showed considerable improvement after phosphorus stripping was introduced at Tower Wood and Ambleside STWs in 1991–1992.

Arctic charr populations

So far, the remediation measures on Windermere have effected a significant reduction in algal productivity, resulting in a discernible improvement in water quality during the later part of the annual growing season. In one sense, the most important measure of remediation success would be a beneficial impact on the populations of Arctic charr, fish of high conservation value and previously showing signs of population decline in the South Basin of the lake (Chapter 6). To study this, a programme to monitor the numbers of pelagic fish in Windermere by using echo-location equipment has been undertaken since 1989. The main results are illustrated on page 100.

Shoals of fish can be identified and removed from the overall counts and, therefore, the method of monitoring to some extent discriminates against shoaling species such as perch and roach. However it does not enable us to identify particular species of fish recorded as individual 'counts'. In the 1990s there has been a steady increase in the numbers of detected fish, particularly during the night, in both basins of Windermere. Marked differences in numbers recorded by day-time and night-time samples are indicative of a major behavioural change, indicating that fish probably move from close to the bed of the lake into the upper parts of the water column during the night. There is no evidence of any daily mass migration of fish from the littoral zone close inshore to the open water.

Catches made with nets prior to 1989 have shown that over ninety percent of the pelagic fish population in Windermere were charr and trout, with charr dominating in both basins. In addition the echo-survey data obtained between 1989 and 1994 were compared with catches of charr made by fishermen and with samples obtained by netting charr on their spawning sites. The comparison revealed significant correlations amongst the data-sets, suggesting that the majority of the pelagic fish detected by echo-surveys during that period were charr. A netting survey carried out in 2001 confirmed that the vast majority of the pelagic fish in the North Basin were charr but in the South Basin the pelagic fish also included some roach and perch.

We conclude that there has been a significant recovery of the Windermere charr populations since the introduction of phosphate stripping and resultant water quality improvement, and that this recovery is most obvious in the South Basin of the lake. The population of roach in Windermere has increased dramatically during recent years and future increases in pelagic fish may be due to this species. The possibility is considered further in Chapter 9, and the need for new research to examine the expansion of roach in Windermere is highlighted.

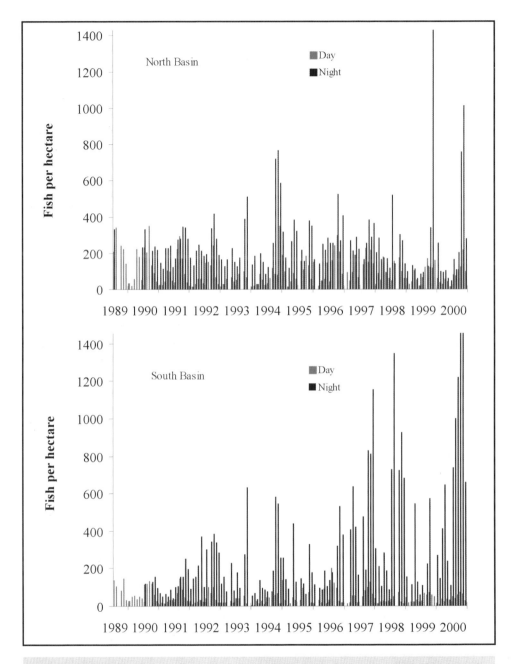

Density of pelagic fish (expressed as numbers of fish per hectare of lake surface) in samples taken during the day (red) and at night (blue), from July 1989 to December 2000 in the North and South Basin of Windermere. Note: only day samples were obtained between August 1989 and May 1990.

Chapter 8
Lake management

It is clear from the earlier chapters that practical management of a lake such as Windermere is a complex matter involving numerous parties, each with its own particular interest and responsibilities. The lake was bought for £6,000 by Henry Leigh Groves OBE in 1938 and given to the general public, a gesture described at the time as "a truly munificent gift". Conflicts of interest will inevitably arise from time to time and their resolution requires difficult decisions to be taken. In such cases it is important to understand the relative roles of the major organisations with an interest in and responsibility for the management of Windermere and its catchment. These range from governmental organisations with clearly defined statutory duties, to voluntary bodies (or individuals) with an interest in certain aspects of the lake and its associated activities. This chapter considers some important management areas and issues, and outlines the roles of key players, but is not intended to be an exhaustive account of all the interested parties. Chapter 9 describes a relatively new initiative which brings together several of these organisations into the Lake District Still Waters Partnership, and outlines the way in which they intend to work together and with other organisations to promote effective management of the lakes and tarns within the Lake District.

Water quality and abstraction

Water quality in Windermere is influenced by direct discharges to the lake, by changes in the catchment and by atmospheric deposition. Naturally, water quality and quantity are inextricably linked and both are sensitive to predicted climate changes. In addition, biologically-driven processes modify and in some cases exacerbate water quality within the lake.

The Environment Agency has an overall responsibility for monitoring, maintaining and improving water quality in the fresh waters of England and Wales. The Agency was created in 1996 by Act of Parliament and given wide-ranging responsibilities for controlling air, land and water pollution and for managing water resources, flood defences and freshwater fisheries across England and Wales. It was formed by amalgamation of the National Rivers Authority, Her Majesty's Inspectorate of Pollution, and Waste Agencies previously under local authority control. It is the Agency's declared policy to work in partnership with other organisations and it has developed several mechanisms to further such collaboration. These include the establishment of advisory committees (such as the Regional Environment Protection Advisory Committee, the Regional Fisheries, Ecology and Recreation Advisory Committee and Area Environment Groups) with representation from a wide range of the user community.

North West Water Ltd (now United Utilities) has a major interest in Windermere, both as a supplier of drinking water and as the principal agency responsible for the treatment and disposal of waste water. These two functions are described in more detail in Chapters 5 and 6, respectively. Waste water generated within the catchment is treated at five sewage treatment works and then discharged into the aquatic environment. The main discharges of treated waste water are at Ambleside (Windermere North Basin) and at Tower Wood (Windermere South Basin). United Utilities works closely with several organisations to minimise the impacts of their operations on the aquatic environment.

Directive 91/27/EEC of the Council of the European Union (the Urban Waste Water Treatment Directive (UWWTD)) aims to protect the aquatic environment from the adverse effects of discharges of waste water (domestic or a mixture of domestic and industrial). It applies to all discharges from population equivalents in excess of two thousand but the timetable for implementation is dependent upon the size of the effluent and the sensitivity of the receiving water. The most urgent cases are waters that are defined as 'sensitive' and receive waste water from a human population in excess of ten thousand. The Directive is implemented in England and Wales through the Urban Waste Water Treatment (England and Wales) Regulations 1994.

The resident population of the Windermere catchment is about seventeen and a half thousand individuals but this is more than doubled at the peak of the tourist season (Chapter 3). Hence, in terms of the human dimension, Windermere certainly qualifies for urgent consideration under the UWWTD. Also, Windermere is very sensitive to some of the nutrients (primarily phosphorus) contained within the treated, discharged waste water, resulting in a deterioration in water quality, to the detriment of the lake's populations of Arctic charr (Chapter 6). Thus Windermere also qualifies for protection under the UWWTD on the grounds of sensitivity and therefore has been designated by the Department of the Environment, Transport and the Regions (DETR), through the Environment Agency (1998 was the deadline for compliance with the regulations). However, by working in partnership with research scientists from the Centre for Ecology and Hydrology and the Freshwater Biological Association, and with the Environment Agency, North West Water implemented tertiary treatment to reduce phosphorus in the major effluents to the lake some seven years before the legal deadline. This action undoubtedly prevented further ecological deterioration and promoted a degree of recovery.

The UWWTD legislation is the first to set standards for the amount of phosphorus discharged to UK waters and, for Windermere, limits the permissible concentration of phosphorus (measured as total phosphorus) in treated waste waters to less than two milligrams per litre. This is an absolute figure that does not take into account the capacity of the receiving water to dilute the effluent and the

Directive sets no targets for the receiving water except that it should give a positive response to remediation measures. Under the terms of the UWWTD the Environment Agency is obliged to organise a suitable water quality monitoring programme to ensure that Windermere does not deteriorate as a result of waste-water effluent discharge. This monitoring programme is currently undertaken by CEH Windermere (Chapter 1) and includes water chemistry, algal populations and an estimate of the numbers of charr in the lake. As shown in Chapter 7, Windermere is clearly responding positively to the tertiary treatment of its incoming effluents.

Another aspect of water quality in Windermere is the extent of contamination by sewage-derived micro-organisms. The Bathing Waters Directive (76/160/EEC) aims to protect human health by reducing microbiological contamination of designated bathing waters. In 1998 (and for the first time in the UK) nine inland bathing waters were designated by DETR, under the Directive. Three of these bathing areas are beaches around Windermere: Miller Ground (North Basin), the YMCA Lakeside (South Basin) and Fell Foot (South Basin). The Directive requires that the water off these beaches must be monitored at least once per fortnight for bacterial contamination during the bathing season but, at the time of writing, the Directive is under revision. The revised document will separate the provisions for maintaining bathing water quality in fresh waters from those for marine bathing waters. The Environment Agency again has responsibility for a monitoring programme and, currently, water samples are examined for total coliforms and faecal coliforms (bacteria derived from the human digestive tract). These bacteria are not necessarily pathogenic but they are indicators of sewage pollution. The Directive requires that there should be no more than ten thousand coliforms and no more than two thousand faecal coliforms per hundred millilitres in ninety-five percent of the samples taken during the bathing season. If the microbiological quality of the bathing water is not met, the Environment Agency can demand further waste-water treatment on the main effluents (such as ultraviolet sterilisation) if, indeed, these are shown to be the main sources of contamination. Further research is needed to ascertain the impact of local sewage effluents from nearby properties on the microbiological quality of the Windermere bathing waters.

Water is abstracted from the North Basin of the lake by United Utilities, treated and then distributed via the main aqueducts to industrial areas further south (Chapter 5). The quality of the supplied water is to drinking-water standards and the supplier is required to demonstrate that the aesthetic, chemical and microbiological quality of the delivered water meets exacting standards set by the Drinking Water Inspectorate. The quantity of water taken from the lake is determined by an abstraction licence, the terms of which are set by the Environment Agency and take into account the need for an adequate flow of water in the River Leven, the outflow from Windermere. Under drought conditions, United Utilities can apply to vary the conditions of their abstraction licence, in the interests of maintaining the public water supply. The Environment Agency is also preparing a new framework for managing water abstraction (Catchment Abstraction Management Schemes (CAMS)) in which the ecological requirements of the waterbody are taken into full consideration. Moreover, CAMS also propose to set strict time limits for the duration of abstraction licences, after which they will be reviewed and re-negotiated.

Landscape and wildlife conservation

English Nature was set up by the Environment Act 1990 with a commitment to give the lead in sustaining and enriching England's natural heritage for all to enjoy now and in the future. It is responsible for identifying Sites of Special Scientific Interest (SSSIs) and promoting the sustainable management of these sites (see Chapter 3 for details of the numerous SSSIs within the Windermere catchment). It also establishes and manages National Nature Reserves, two of which occur within the Windermere catchment, and implements the UK Biodiversity Action Plan. English Nature provides advice and information on nature conservation to Government and other organisations, and works with equivalent organisations in Scotland and Wales through the Joint Nature Conservation Committee (JNCC). Local management is based on a team structure, with the Cumbrian team located in Kendal. A key English Nature document is 'Wildlife and freshwater – an agenda for sustainable management', published in 1997. This reflects the fact that one-third of all SSSIs are freshwater sites.

The Environment Agency also has a strong commitment to nature conservation – indeed, the Agency's principal aim is to contribute to sustainable development by protecting and enhancing the environment as a whole. To achieve this the Agency has overall statutory duties towards conservation in its role as both regulator and operator, plus a duty generally to promote the conservation of water-related habitats and associated wildlife.

The Lake District National Park was established in 1951 and is the largest National Park in Great Britain. It is administered by the Lake District National Park Authority, with its headquarters in Kendal. The LDNPA is an independent body (a mixture of elected County and District councillors and appointed Members) that is part of the local government of the Lake District. As such it has some but not all of the powers and duties of other councils but, of course, its activities are largely concentrated within the boundaries of the National Park. The Windermere catchment lies totally within the National Park and, therefore, the LDNPA has a major influence on activities relating to Windermere. It has statutory purposes to conserve and enhance the natural beauty, wildlife and cultural heritage of the National Park and to promote opportunities for the understanding and enjoyment of the special qualities of the area by the public.

All public bodies are required to have regard to National Park purposes when undertaking activities within the Park, and if there appears to be conflict between the two purposes they are required to attach greater weight to that of conserving the natural beauty, wildlife and cultural heritage of the area. The LDNPA undertakes practical conservation work (both natural environment and cultural heritage) in the Windermere catchment and provides direct support for the management of recreation, including the repair and maintenance of rights of way. Public understanding is promoted through a variety of facilities, including a network of Tourist Information Centres and the Lake District Visitor Centre at Brockhole, on the east shore of Windermere. The LDNPA also operates a Ranger Service on the lake, which is there to assist the public using the lake and to enforce existing bye-laws.

The National Trust is an important landowner within the Windermere catchment, managing large tracts of woodland along the western shore of the lake. Founded in 1895 by three Victorian philanthropists, the National Trust is the UK's largest registered charity. Because of concerns about the impact of uncontrolled development and industrialisation, the Trust was set up to act as a guardian for the nation in the acquisition and protection of threatened coastline, countryside and buildings. The Trust relies heavily on more than thirty-eight thousand voluntary workers nationwide and is committed to environmental conservation work and habitat improvement. The national headquarters are in London (from which the organisation publishes its Annual Report); the North West Regional Office is at Grasmere, within the Windermere catchment.

The Cumbria Wildlife Trust (formerly The Lake District Naturalists' Trust, Cumbria Naturalists' Trust, and Cumbria Trust for Nature Conservation) is one of forty-five sister trusts across the UK. A charity with over six thousand members, the trust represents more than one percent of the total population within the county and organises a programme of events (practical conservation, walks, talks and conferences) throughout the year. Cumbria Wildlife Trust works in partnership with landowners, local authorities, other conservation organisations and businesses to conserve wildlife everywhere in Cumbria and manages around forty nature reserves. As with several other organisations, the Trust is sent the details of all the planning applications that are made in Cumbria and considers the implications of the proposed development for wildlife. If a development would cause serious damage to a wildlife site the Trust would object to the development. Where possible the Trust works with developers to ensure that there is minimal damage or disturbance to the site.

The Friends of the Lake District is a registered charity with some seven thousand members, committed to promote and organise concerted action for the protection and conservation of the landscape and natural beauty of the Lake District and the County of Cumbria as a whole, and co-operate with other bodies having similar objectives or interests. Friends of the Lake District also represents the Council for the Protection of Rural England in Cumbria.

Direct use of the lake

Windermere falls within the administrative control of South Lakeland District Council (SLDC) which, as the owner of the lakebed (on behalf of the general public), has a major influence on the day-to-day management of the lake. This includes the control of most of the boat traffic on the lake, although the relevant legislation for navigation on the lake is the responsibility of the LDNPA. The District Council also produces information leaflets on most aspects of recreational activities on the lake, including the need for sensitive management for nature conservation (see above). SLDC controls the only public launching slipways on the lake, manages the numerous boat moorings and operates a Lake Warden service to ensure the safety and security of everyone on the lake. The larger passenger launches and 'steamers' (now diesel-powered) on the lake are operated independently from the SLDC, but within the legislative framework of the Windermere bye-laws and under Department of Trade and Industry regulations.

So far we have considered organisations with statutory responsibilities for lake management and planning or those with strong conservation interests. Direct recreational activity on the lake primarily involves two sports, boating and angling, of which the former is the dominant pastime. The history of boating on Windermere is described in Chapter 5, as are the protracted plans to introduce a 10 mph speed limit for the whole of the lake. All boating activity (power or sail) on a national scale comes under the auspices of the Royal Yachting Association but, at a local level, there are several well-organised clubs and associations that control their own members' activities. In addition there are a number of outdoor activity centres such as the YMCA at Lakeside, Tower Wood Outdoor Pursuits Centre, Great Tower Scout Camp, Ghyll Head Outdoor Pursuits Centre, Brathay Exploration Group and others who all use the lake for activities and courses. Members of the general public are free to use the lake at any time provided that all boats are launched at a recognised public or privately-owned landing site and, in the case of boats with engines, that the boat has been suitably registered. The Windermere (Lake) Bye-laws define the law on the lake with respect to lighting, navigation, conduct in restricted visibility, speed limits, water skiing, noise, zone restrictions and waste disposal from a boat. Mandatory zone restrictions are limited to speed restrictions in certain areas of the lake – zones to benefit nature conservation are dependent upon voluntary observance of the requirements. Parascending is not allowed on the lake without the prior, written approval of the LDNPA, and the use of towed inflatables for recreational purposes is prohibited.

Angling on Windermere is subject to all the national rules and regulations operated by the Environment Agency, covering licences, fishing seasons, angling techniques etc. Fishing from the shoreline is permitted but only with the owners' permission. The National Trust, South Lakeland District Council and the Lake District National Park Authority allow angling from their land, and the Windermere, Ambleside and District Angling Association manages one section of shoreline fishing in the South Basin. Fishing from boats is also permitted. All rivers entering or leaving the lake are private and a permit to fish must be obtained for these waters. Chapter 4 provides information on the natural fish populations in the lake and Chapter 5 traces the history of commercial fisheries on Windermere. Fishing activities on the lake are now restricted to angling for pleasure and the semi-commercial charr fishery.

Windermere is also used for sub-aqua sports but, given the extent of boat traffic on the lake, it is essential that surface marker buoys are used at all times. If diving from a boat, an 'A' flag must be hoisted whenever a diver is in the water. All items found on the bed of the lake are the property of South Lakeland District Council and may not be removed without permission. At a national level, the sport is governed by the British Sub-Aqua Club.

The Cumbria Tourist Board is the official tourist board for the county and is jointly funded by the English Tourist Board, local authorities within the county, and private sector members from all areas of the tourist industry. The Board currently has two thousand members and its overall objective is to promote tourism in the area (including the Windermere catchment). It aims to achieve this through vigorous marketing and promotion, objective measurement and research, integrated development and sustainable tourism. At the time of writing, the tourist industry is experiencing a marked downturn because of access restrictions introduced to limit the spread of foot and mouth disease in the region. The concept of sustainable tourism is crucial to the management of Windermere, if the pressures of a growing industry are not to damage the very asset on which the industry is based.

Catchment management

The point has been made repeatedly that Windermere is extremely sensitive to changes that may occur outside the physical confines of the lake itself. Therefore it is essential that a co-ordinated approach is adopted by all those with an interest in further development within the Windermere catchment.

Cumbria County Council has administrative responsibility for the whole of Cumbria, a county that includes not only the Lake District National Park but also part of the Yorkshire Dales National Park, as well as the industrialised west coast and Furness areas and the mainly agricultural Eden valley. The administrative headquarters of Cumbria County Council are located in Carlisle. Cumbria County

Political boundaries in Cumbria.

Council has responsibilities for services such as education, highways, economic development and social care across the whole of Cumbria. The Lake District National Park Authority has many responsibilities for the management of the lake (see above) but the maintenance of major highways (including the Windermere ferry) is undertaken by the County Council.

Working with other organisations, the LDNPA has a major input to traffic management policies and supports the move away from private cars to public transport and cycling schemes. A team of Rangers and Estate Workers is complemented by the Voluntary Wardens Service to assist with the maintenance of rights of way, giving advice to landowners and the public, and undertaking conservation projects. A key role of the Authority is in planning control to ensure that local development is of a scale and design that respects local character and does not detract from the special qualities of the National Park.

The primary use of land within the catchment is for agriculture, and current management systems are strongly influenced by subsidies and incentives, which are an integral part of the Common Agricultural Policy. Agenda 2000 reforms agreed by the Government include a shift of resources from the direct support of agricultural production to support for conservation through 'agri-environment schemes', and to regeneration of the rural economy. These changes are included in the England Rural Development Plan, which includes a chapter on the North West, published by the Ministry of Agriculture in 2000. In recent years, farmers have been faced by seriously declining incomes as a result of reductions in the price of products, the effects of bovine spongiform encephalopathy (BSE or 'mad cow disease') and the strong pound, all of which have affected exports. The very difficult problems facing the industry have been compounded by the outbreak of foot and mouth disease in 2001. The way in which the government and individual farmers respond to the situation will have a significant bearing on future land use. Opportunities to rebuild farming in ways that incorporate more sustainable practices could bring significant benefits. However, there is serious concern that a continuing move towards larger farm units and the demands for rural residential property could have a damaging impact on the landscape of the National Park and the social and economic well-being of its local communities.

Compared with many parts of the UK, much of the Windermere catchment is well wooded. Timber production has also suffered by a decline in product prices and the commercial management of smaller woodland estates in particular has become very difficult. Much of the woodland in the catchment is managed for conservation and amenity purposes, and such uses may benefit from changes in the grant regimes operated by the Forestry Commission to support the implementation of the England Forestry Strategy published in 2000. In the National Park virtually all new planting or deforestation is the subject of European Environmental Assessment Regulations. The implementation of these rests with the Forestry Commission, which also is the principal body for funding forestry and woodland projects although, increasingly, local organisations such as the National Trust and other local conservation bodies look to additional funding from a wide range of sources to pursue their objectives.

Strategic forward planning

Given the number of interested and involved parties, it is important that future planning is undertaken in as co-ordinated a manner as possible. Most of the organisations mentioned above undertake their own strategic planning reviews and some do this in conjunction with other partners. The Lake District National Park Authority is the unitary planning authority for the National Park. It produces a Structure Plan jointly with Cumbria County Council, which sets out the broad framework to guide future development within the area. More detailed policies, which set out the criteria to direct and assess particular types of development, are contained in the Lake District National Park Local Plan. The LDNPA is also required by law to produce a National Park Management Plan. This brings together a vision for the area, and objectives, policies and proposals covering a wide range of subjects that influence the conservation and public enjoyment of the National Park and the way these needs integrate with the social and economic well-being of its local communities.

The Environment Agency is committed to developing Local Environment Agency Plans, based on catchment management, for the specific management of river basins. The development of LEAPs involves extensive consultation with the general public and the plans are reviewed annually and revised every five years. The Agency, a national organisation with headquarters in Bristol, is also organised on a hierarchical, regional basis, further subdivided into Areas. The North Area of the North West Region is primarily responsible for matters related to the Cumbrian lakes (including Windermere) and operates from Area Headquarters in Penrith. Management of the Windermere catchment is an integral part of the South Cumbria LEAP, a document that itemises key environmental issues related to the lake and its catchment and is, in itself, an important source of environmental information. In addition, the Environment Agency has also recently developed a Lakes Business Plan reviewing all the major lakes of the Lake District and prioritising the actions required for their protection and/or restoration. The aim for the Cumbrian lakes is "to protect the best and improve the rest". Again, this planning is undertaken in partnership with other organisations – indeed, the Environment Agency has a specific duty under the 1995 Environment Act to have regard to National Park purposes.

The plan that most directly concerns the management of the lake is the Windermere Management Plan (1981), prepared jointly by the owners, South Lakeland District Council, and other organisations. It covers the basic principles of lake management with an objective "To make provision for the enjoyment of Windermere by the public without prejudice to the character of the lake, its tranquillity and its nature conservation value". More specifically, the Management Plan deals with issues of access to the water, nature conservation for waterfowl, zoning and speed limits on the lake, bathing, mooring and navigation and wardening. Some of the management issues in the Plan have since been superseded by the 10 mph speed limit (Chapter 5) and the bathing water designation (see p. 103).

As a final comment in this section on forward planning, a new piece of European legislation will have a major impact on the way in which we manage the UK freshwater environment. Introduced in 2000, the Water Framework Directive is scheduled for full implementation by 2015. The Directive (2000/60/EC) is one of the most substantial pieces of legislation ever produced concerning European waters, and the UK has to bring into force the necessary domestic provisions to comply with the Directive by December 2003. The Directive will require objectives to be set for all waterbodies, with a particular emphasis on ecological quality for surface waters. It will be based on comprehensive river basin management plans (involving many partners) and requires member states to ensure that there is no deterioration in the ecological status of waterbodies.

The need for partnership

It should be apparent to the reader that many different, interested parties are involved in the management of Windermere, often with conflicting (albeit legitimate) interests. Any management strategy ought to consider all points of view and accommodate as many of these as possible. Inevitably, conflicts of interest will continue to arise in the future and those with responsibility for the practical management of the lake must achieve an appropriate integration of social, economic and environmental objectives to sustain the lake's qualities. Work to achieve such a solution will require effective communication and co-operation amongst a very wide range of interested parties. It is important that the progress already made to restore the health of England's largest lake will be consolidated and further developed. Any actions need to be monitored to check whether they have indeed achieved the desired results and the understanding that flows from such work will assist decisions required elsewhere.

Chapter 9
Our future heritage

This book has traced the origins of England's largest natural lake, and described some of its ecology and conservation value. Inevitably, Windermere has been subjected to a series of environmental impacts and, arguably, the greatest of these has been nutrient enrichment during the last fifty years. We have seen how the growth of tourism has led to the requirement for a more effective waste-water treatment and disposal system in the catchment and how this has resulted in an additional phosphate load to the lake. The consequence of this has been a stimulation of algal growth leading to water quality deterioration and a decline in the populations of the glacial relict fish, the Arctic charr. Recent remedial measures to remove phosphorus from the main treated sewage effluents entering the lake have halted, and to some extent reversed, this negative trend. This chapter now considers the future and asks whether the measures already in place are sufficient to assure the long-term health of the lake. New and emerging environmental issues are considered in relation to their potential impact on Windermere and key areas for research are identified. Finally, a plea is made for a more integrated approach to lake management – the lessons learned from Windermere are applicable in principle to the other lakes of the English Lake District and, indeed, more generally.

Is phosphorus stripping sufficient to improve water quality?

The weight of evidence shows that the STW effluents from Ambleside and Tower Wood are, jointly, the most important potential sources of soluble phosphorus within the catchment. The installation of ferric sulphate precipitation to remove phosphorus from the treated effluents has undoubtedly caused a significant and sustained reduction in the background concentrations of phosphorus in the lake and water quality has improved, to the benefit of the charr populations in the lake. However, the decline in phosphorus levels (from 30-40 micrograms per litre to approximately 20 micrograms per litre in the South Basin) is not as great as might have been anticipated and the reasons for this must be considered. This issue assumes increasing importance because, as predicted, Windermere is clearly sensitive to nutrient manipulation and further decreases in phosphorus levels will, almost certainly, result in additional water quality improvements.

Phosphorus stripping, by dosing with ferric salts, has the potential to remove more than ninety percent of the phosphorus from secondary sewage effluents under optimal conditions (Chapter 7). However, an examination of the effectiveness of the process at both Ambleside and Tower Wood STWs shows that such efficiency is rarely, if ever, achieved for prolonged periods. In general, both works normally meet the phosphorus discharge consents set by the

Environment Agency, in line with EU policy (under the Urban Waste Water Treatment Directive), although Tower Wood appears to have a greater difficulty in achieving this than Ambleside. Phosphorus stripping is most effective when the sewage effluent is at its most concentrated, and any dilution of the effluent by surface water has the potential to reduce the efficiency of the process. Whether this is primarily a physico-chemical dilution phenomenon affecting chemical precipitation and adsorption to the floc, or whether it is because of reduced contact time during the overall process, is still a matter for debate. An examination of the relationship between the concentration of phosphorus in the raw sewage entering Ambleside STW, and previous rainfall, shows that when rainfall is high it tends to dilute the initial phosphorus concentrations in the sewage. In turn this reduces the efficiency of the phosphorus stripping process, and efficiencies actually drop to below twenty percent during some (but not all) periods when the initial phosphorus concentration of the incoming sewage is relatively low. Moreover, during wet weather an unknown proportion of

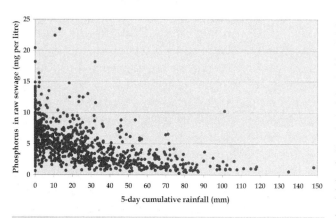

Phosphorus concentrations in raw sewage at Ambleside Sewage Treatment Works, related to previous rainfall over a 5-day period.

the sewage phosphorus load enters the lake via storm-water overflows, and further research is needed to estimate the size of the nutrient load which is bypassing the waste-water treatment process and entering the lake directly. This should include modelling the impact of storm-water overflow on the overall nutrient budget of the lake.

Thus further management options requiring consideration will eventually need to include minimising the ingress of surface water into the sewerage network in the Windermere catchment. At one end of the spectrum this might focus on the main points of intentional ingress and, at the other end, focus on the case for a completely separate foul sewer. An alternative might be to increase the storage of storm water, followed by subsequent treatment through the established STWs. Clearly, any option must be fully costed against realistic aims and appropriate ecological endpoints in the lake, and the most cost-effective solution(s) must be considered as part of the Asset Management Planning process. This would involve wide consultation and close collaboration between the Environment Agency, United Utilities and OFWAT (Office of Water Services).

Developing environmental issues

This book has focused, to a considerable extent, on the issue of nutrient enrichment in Windermere. However, other factors (local, regional and global) also have the potential to change the natural ecology of the lake, either independently or by interacting with the effects of eutrophication.

Global warming and climate change

The consensus of scientific opinion (represented by the UN's Intergovernmental Panel on Climate Change) is now of the view that human activities have caused discernible changes in global climate, primarily as the direct result of atmospheric pollution. Greenhouse gases such as carbon dioxide, methane and nitrous oxide have all increased demonstrably in the atmosphere since the industrial revolution and concentrations are continuing to rise at an alarming rate. The average global temperature has increased by some 0.6°C during the last one hundred and fifty years (the fastest rate of change for at least 2,000 years) and even one of the more conservative current models predicts a further rise of at least 3 to 4°C during the next century. Inevitably, such a temperature increase would have direct impacts on the ecology of Windermere, but perhaps the most important aspect of climate change (and the most difficult to predict) is the effect on rainfall patterns. Current expectations are for *increased* annual rainfall in the north-west of Britain, with the greatest increase during the winter months. Indeed, the summer period may be characterised by increasing periods of drought.

We know from existing studies that Windermere is sensitive to relatively subtle climatic changes. The course of the Gulf Stream, as it tracks across the North Atlantic towards Europe, varies from year to year.

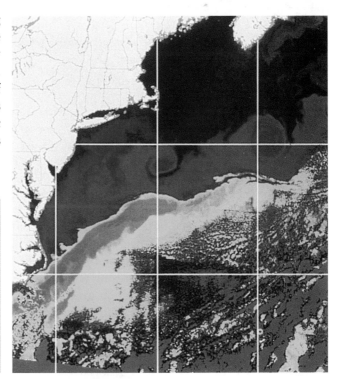

A satellite thermal image of the Gulf Stream. Orange and yellow depict warm sea water (20–30°C) as it drifts north and east across the North Atlantic. Blue colours depict cooler water. The uncoloured area on the left of the picture shows part of the coastline of North America, extending from Nova Scotia (top right) down to Chesapeake Bay and Cape Hatteras.

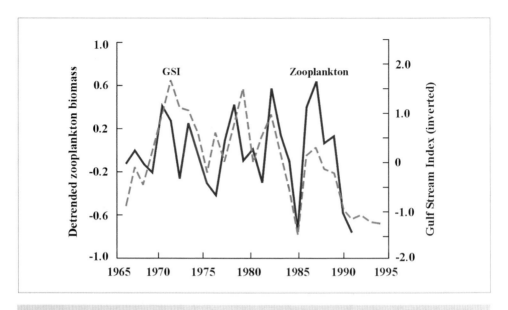

The biomass of zooplankton in Windermere is closely correlated with the position (latitude) of the Gulf Stream in the North Atlantic as it gradually moves northwards and then southwards during each decade. In the drawing, the geographical position of the Gulf Stream has been expressed as an index (GSI).

In years when the Gulf Stream is displaced towards the northern limits of its range, the spring months at the latitude of Windermere tend to be dominated by calm dry periods resulting in stronger thermal stratification of the lake (Chapter 3). The opposite is true when the Gulf Stream is towards the southerly limits of its distribution – in such years the spring months tend to be wet and windy, and thermal stratification in Windermere is weaker. The ecology of the lake mirrors some of these differences, as zooplankton populations are larger under conditions of weaker stratification and, in turn, these have 'knock on' effects on the growth of young fish, particularly perch. With this demonstrable sensitivity to climatic signals, Windermere will inevitably respond to future climate change, possibly in ways that are not fully understood at the present time.

Long dry summers could favour the growth of nuisance blue-green algae but, in general, effects of changes in rainfall patterns and the timing and intensity of wind-mixing are likely to be of more importance than the effects of temperature *per se* on plankton communities. The upper thermal limit for survival of charr eggs (8°C) is unlikely to be exceeded during the winter months but a warmer climate could increase the growth rate of some of the fish in the lake. However, growth models for young sea trout living in the streams within the catchment suggest that a 4°C rise in mean temperature would inhibit growth in these fish, resulting in smaller (and more vulnerable) smolts migrating to sea.

Interestingly, the climate change models predict a *decrease* in rainfall in the south-east of England, exaggerating the existing gradient of water resources from the north-west to the south-east. In addition, higher temperatures will almost certainly influence our patterns of water usage. One possible effect of global warming could be an increased pressure on the use of Windermere and other north-west waterbodies for water supply to other parts of the country (at the moment it is largely used as a reserve – see Chapter 5 for details). The whole issue of global warming is poorly understood, both in terms of probable environmental and socio-economic impacts.

Micropollutants

Any pollution incident that directly causes a fish kill immediately hits the headlines. However, these days most effects of pollution are quite subtle and may be caused by a complex mixture or 'cocktail' of chemicals, each one at a concentration that normally would not be considered dangerous. Such pollutants, often referred to as micropollutants, may also accumulate in the organisms of the food web, increasing significantly in concentration in the top predators. The effect of pesticides on eggshell thinning in birds of prey is a good example of such bioaccumulation, ultimately resulting in damage at the top end of a food chain. In this case, regulations were subsequently introduced to ban the use of those chemicals shown to be the cause of the problem. As humans create more and more new chemicals, most of which will inevitably find their way into the environment, the potential for damage to aquatic species will increase. Polychlorinated biphenyls (PCBs), industrial chemicals used particularly in the electrical industry, are now found in the body tissues of animals at some of the most remote polar regions of the planet – geographic distance is of little protection against such ubiquitous pollutants. Recent evidence from the Netherlands suggests that polybrominated flame retardants are now contaminating large parts of the environment (although their effects on wildlife are largely unknown) and constant vigilance is required on the manufacture, use and disposal of such chemicals. In Windermere, chemicals indicative of oil pollution (polycyclic aromatic hydrocarbons (PAHs) and aliphatic hydrocarbons) can be detected in the sediments. The former are produced by the combustion of petroleum products; the latter are characteristic of oil spillage and road runoff. Increases in aliphatic hydrocarbons in the sediments during the 20th century reflect the development of the leisure boat industry on Windermere but, as far as the author is aware, there is no evidence that the level of contamination is having significant effects on the ecology of the lake.

Certain types of micropollutants (the so-called 'endocrine disrupters') can interfere with an animal's endocrine system – the vital network of hormones that controls much of the animal's physiology, development and behaviour. Environmental oestrogens (compounds that mimic the effects of the natural steroid hormone, 17β-oestradiol) have attracted increasing attention in recent years, because of their potential feminising effects on male fish. Many undiluted sewage effluents possess oestrogenic activity and, in extreme cases, this has resulted in a degree of feminisation of male fish in some UK and European rivers. The molecules responsible for these effects include natural oestrogens secreted from the female component of the human population, a synthetic oestrogen from the contraceptive pill, and one or more breakdown products from industrial detergents. In Windermere, the degree of dilution of treated sewage effluent is such that male fish in the lake are unlikely to be affected, but the whole issue of endocrine disruption emphasises the sensitivity of aquatic wildlife to man-made (and natural) chemicals.

Another potent form of endocrine disruption has been associated with the use of certain antifouling paints on boats. The key component of such paints is tributyl tin which, as we now understand, can cause a catastrophic disruption of sexual development in certain species of shellfish. Populations of dogwhelk *Nucella lapillus* have been decimated around parts of the UK's coastline, particularly in areas associated with shipping lanes and boat marinas. Tributyl tin has now been banned for use on small boats and therefore no longer poses a threat to the molluscs in Windermere. Nevertheless it is yet another reminder of the potential of man-made chemicals to have adverse and long-term impacts on the environment at extremely low concentrations.

Introduced species

Chapter 4 describes the 'natural' colonisation of Windermere by a few, non-native invertebrates and plants. However, human intervention (probably in the form of anglers using live fish as bait for pike) is almost certainly responsible for the deliberate introduction of new fish species into the area. Such acts are not only illegal, they are totally irresponsible. For example, the relatively recent appearance of ruffe *Gymnocephalus cernuus* and roach *Rutilus rutilus* in Bassenthwaite Lake creates a new predator and competitor, respectively, for the rare vendace *Coregonus albula*. This problem has been exacerbated by the even more recent appearance of dace *Leuciscus leuciscus* in the same lake.

Roach are now a significant component of the fish populations present in Windermere. The origins of these fish are not as clear as they are for Bassenthwaite Lake because roach have been occasionally caught in the lake during the last thirty years (and may have been present for a longer time). However, there is little doubt that this species is currently undergoing something of a population explosion in Windermere (as it has done in parts of Ireland after its introduction there) and research is urgently needed to understand the potential effects of the roach on the other species of fish in the lake. This should include possible interactions with the charr and trout.

DAVID LEWINS 89

A fine specimen of a roach, taken from an original painting.

With regard to the potential effects of roach, there is still a requirement for fundamental research on the Windermere trout populations, if these are to be managed in a sustainable manner. Moreover, we need to explore the likely impacts of nutrient control and climate change on the fish populations of Windermere. Further introductions of fish species must be avoided and this will require careful policing by the Environment Agency.

Chapter 4 also describes how the aquatic plant community in Windermere has changed over the last century, particularly with the successive appearance of two species of Canadian pondweed, *Elodea canadensis* and *E. nuttallii*. A further potential threat to the native plant community of the lake is the swamp stonecrop *Crassula helmsii*. Originally a native of Australia, this plant has been commercially available to the water gardener since 1927 and has since spread into natural waterbodies. Following the finding of its first naturalised site in Essex in the mid-1950s, this invasive species has spread northwards and westwards and is now colonising Derwent Water in the Lake District. It is a particularly successful invader capable of rapid growth from small pieces of the plant, with a range of habitats from damp soil to deep water (up to 3 metres). Particular care must be taken by anyone enjoying water-related activities in the area not to transfer inadvertently any plant material from Derwent Water to Windermere (or to any other waterbody, for that matter). Once introduced, it is almost impossible to eradicate.

Disappearance of reedbeds around Grass Holme, a small island about halfway down the western side of the South Basin. The upper photograph was taken in 1980 and the lower photograph was taken in 2001.

Reedbed decline

Certain areas of shoreline vegetation, and reedbeds in particular, are important components of the habitat mosaic of Windermere (Chapter 4). More specifically, reedbeds offer a secure refuge for overwintering wildfowl and a nesting habitat for breeding species. Recent concerns over the decline of reedbeds around the margins of the lake have been fuelled by the relatively recent loss of reedbeds from around Grass Holme, an island in the South Basin of Windermere, so-named because of its abundant growth of reeds. The issue has been compounded by reports of a similar problem in other parts of Europe. However, on closer inspection it would appear that the decline of reedbeds in Windermere may be a long-standing problem – contemporary accounts of wildfowling activities on the lake during the First World War and in the 1920s express concern about the relative decline of this particular habitat. No clear explanation for this change has been put forward so far, although possible factors must include nutrient enrichment, changes in lake-level regimes, erosion through boating activities, climate change and disease, or any combination of these. This is a subject requiring further research.

Sustainable development

Much has been written about the concept of 'sustainable development' and the phrase features strongly in environmental policy statements of most organisations, whether in the public or private sector. However, how many people stop to think what this concept really means? It is human nature to wish to continually improve our individual comfort, convenience and quality of life, and technology has given us some of the tools to achieve this. At the same time, most believe that we also have a moral duty to ensure that our activities do not compromise the ability of future generations to meet their aspirations – in effect we are custodians of the planet for our children and grandchildren. Sustainable development formalises these ideas and a widely accepted definition of sustainable development is "development that meets the needs of the present without compromising the ability of future generations to meet their own needs".

A key component of the quality of life for many people is a healthy, natural environment and, therefore, tensions frequently arise from the differing goals of individuals and organisations. In the context of Windermere, the need for a safe, effective and affordable waste-water disposal system versus the requirement to safeguard water quality in the lake, is a good example. Similar observations could be made about the 10 mph speed limit legislation (Chapter 8). In such cases, not only do we have to balance the conflict of interests within the current generation but we also have to consider whether our decisions today will compromise the next generation's management options. A major constraint in making such management decisions is the lack of agreed methodologies for calculating, in economic terms, the value of a healthy environment. In other words "What price a kingfisher?" Whilst it is anathema for many people to consider wildlife in such terms, without an agreed methodology it is difficult to make direct comparisons with other aspects of the use of a public amenity such as Windermere, for which financial values can be calculated. Clearly, this is an important area for future socio-economic research. Of course, high profile species such as kingfishers and otters (and, indeed, Arctic charr) are not only inherently valuable in their own right, they are indicators of a healthy environment. As with many issues, compromises will have to be made – these are invariably difficult to achieve but are most likely to gain acceptance if they are the result of partnership and open dialogue. In the case of lake management, such partnerships must reflect the views of interested parties on a catchment-wide basis. The Lake District Still Waters Partnership has come together to begin to address some of these issues. Its involvement in the publication of this book demonstrates the belief of the partners that there is a need for more accessible information on the often complex issues involved in the management of lakes, so that the decisions being taken are better understood by a wider audience.

The Lake District Still Waters Partnership

The Partnership was created in 1999 and, at the time of writing, has seven core members: the Lake District National Park Authority, the Environment Agency, English Nature, the National Trust, North West Water (now United Utilities), the Centre for Ecology and Hydrology, and the Freshwater Biological Association. The last two organisations in the Partnership provide objective scientific information and advice and their background is outlined in Chapter 1. Further details of the other organisations in the Partnership are given in Chapter 8. The Partnership was brought together following a suggestion from the Environment Agency during its discussions with the Lake District National Park Authority on the development of the Lake District National Park Management Plan (1999).

The Partnership's vision is to protect and, where necessary, enhance this resource by promoting sustainable management and use of the lakes and tarns and their surrounding catchments. The representatives of organisations in the Partnership recognise that the statutory responsibilities of the Partners, and the regulations and procedures under which they operate could, from time to time, raise conflicts of interest. Examples include the regulatory roles of some organisations over other Partners within the Partnership, and the fact that some organisations may commission research on the basis of competitive tenders when others are potential contractors for such work. Thus, participation in the Partnership is on the understanding that any representative of any of the Partners may withdraw from the discussion of any topic, site or proposal if it causes difficulties in relation to their role and responsibilities. Moreover, any representative of any one of the Partners may request the group to ask another Partner to withdraw from discussions if there is a potential conflict of interests (decision to request withdrawal is decided by a majority vote) and any discussions will be without prejudice to any formal processes in which the parent organisations may be involved. An important part of its work is to improve communication between the Partners, identify those areas where there is a clear consensus, and to work towards agreed positions and actions that can be reported and implemented collectively. The Partnership is not intended to be exclusive and other established partnerships will continue to take the lead on individual lakes. Other organisations will be involved in the work of the Partnership in a variety of different ways, depending on the issues under consideration, and it will continue to explore ways of engaging the interest of a wider audience.

This book is a part of that process. It was conceived as part of the celebrations to commemorate the 50th Anniversary of designation of the Lake District National

Park. The manner in which those celebrations have been so devastatingly interrupted by an outbreak of foot and mouth disease emphasises the vulnerability of the rural economy and the difficulty of predicting the future. The story of Windermere is also a salutary reminder of the fact that our basic resources such as water, and our finest landscapes and wildlife communities, need very careful management and investment. The Lake District's lakes and tarns are, collectively, an internationally important ecological, aesthetic, recreational and cultural resource. They contribute a great deal to the identity and special qualities of the Lake District National Park. Our ability to deal with the varied pressures and changes that affect them will have a very significant bearing on the quality and character of the National Park in fifty years time.

Acknowledgements

Given the breadth of the subject matter of this book, it is inevitable that its production has involved a large number of individuals.

The author is grateful to fellow members of the Lake District Still Waters Partnership for their guidance, advice and encouragement during the production of the book. More specifically I thank John Pinder (Environment Agency), Alan Fishwick and Phil Taylor (LDNPA), Allan Stewart (English Nature), David Crawshaw (United Utilities), Fiona Southern and Kevin Reid (National Trust), and Roger Sweeting (FBA), who also developed the business plan for the book.

Data were provided by Nicky Chapman, Ken Clarke, Janice Fletcher, Glen George, Dianne Hewitt, Ian McCulloch, Julie Parker and Colin Reynolds (CEH), Phil Taylor, Mick Donn and Alan Fishwick (LDNPA), Allan Stewart (EN), Jim Maguire, Peter Miller and Steve Phelps (South Lakeland District Council), David Crawshaw, Alan Chester, Ray Morris, Ken Shephard, Frank Everett and Louise Smith (UU), Ian Pettman and Karen Rouen (FBA), Ben Bayliss (EA), and David and Diana Matthews.

Many of the photographs used to illustrate this book were taken by the author and by colleagues based at The Ferry House and the River Laboratory in Dorset. In particular, the work of Trevor Furnass should be acknowledged. Over the years he has photographed many subjects for the FBA, IFE and CEH Windermere, including the scenes of Windermere North Basin on p. 1 and Elterwater on p. 22, which captured magical moments on film for all to see and enjoy. Trevor also took the snow-scene of Windermere in winter that appears on the covers of the book. Special thanks and acknowledgements for photographic material are also made to Hilda Canter-Lund, Malcolm Elliott, David Livingstone and John Lund (FBA), Ken Clarke, Bland Finlay and Jon Bass (CEH), Ronald Mitchell, Peter Guy, Chris Sodo and Phil Taylor (LDNPA), and David Hay (FRS Freshwater Laboratory, Pitlochry). Copyright is acknowledged for illustrations used on pages iii and 21 (Hunting Aerofilms Ltd) and page 16 (GetMapping.com.plc). In addition, Graham Blenkarn provided samples of original charr baits. Ben James, Peter Allen and David Abel (CEH), and Bev Armer, David Thornton, Roger Johnson and Fred Tattersall (Royal Windermere Yacht Club) facilitated photographic opportunities on Windermere. The original artwork was produced by Yvonne Dickens (CEH), to whom the author gives particular thanks for her skill and hard work.

Critical comments on early drafts of the manuscript were received from Stephen Maberly, Peter Matthiessen, Colin Reynolds and Ian Winfield (CEH), John Pinder (EA), Malcolm Elliott, Elizabeth Haworth, John Lund and Roger Sweeting (FBA), Alan Fishwick, John Hodgson, Andrew Lowe and Phil Taylor (LDNPA), Allan Stewart (NT) and David Crawshaw and John Sanders (UU).

Joint financial support for the book's production was provided by the Environment Agency and United Utilities, with additional input from the Centre for Ecology and Hydrology, the Freshwater Biological Association and English Nature.

Finally, the author is extremely grateful to the editor, David Sutcliffe (FBA), for his overall guidance, critical comments and attention to detail. The quality of the final production bears testimony to David's knowledge and experience.

Suggested further reading

Canter-Lund, H. & Lund, J. W. G. (1995). *Freshwater Algae. Their Microscopic World Explored*. Biopress Ltd, Bristol. 380pp. ISBN 0 948737 25 5.

English Nature (1997). *Wildlife and Fresh Water – an Agenda for Sustainable Management*. ISBN 1 85716 260 9.

Fryer, G. (1991). *A Natural History of the Lakes, Tarns and Streams of the English Lake District*. The Freshwater Biological Association, Ambleside, Cumbria. 368pp. ISBN 0 900386 50 9.

Gray, N. F. (1999). *Water Technology. An Introduction for Environmental Scientists and Engineers*. Arnold Publishers, New York. 547pp. ISBN 0 340 67645 0.

Heaton Cooper, W. (1966). *The Lakes*. Frederick Warne & Co Ltd, London. 228pp.

Higham, N. J. (1986). *The Northern Counties to AD 1000 (Regional History of England)*. Longman, London. 392 pp. ISBN 0582 49275 0.

HMSO (1994). *Sustainable Development. The UK Strategy*. HMSO Publications. 268pp.

Kipling, C. (1972). The commercial fisheries of Windermere. *Transactions of the Cumberland and Westmorland Antiquarian and Archaeological Society*, Volume LXXII, 156-204.

Macan, T. T. (1970). *Biological Studies of the English Lakes*. Longman Group Limited, London. 260pp. ISBN 582 46019 0.

Pattinson, G. H. (1981). *The Great Age of Steam on Windermere*. The Windermere Nautical Trust. ISBN 0 907796 00 1.

Reynolds, C. S. & Irish, A. E. (2000). *The Phytoplankton of Windermere (English Lake District)*. The Freshwater Biological Association, Ambleside, Cumbria. 73pp. ISBN 0 900386 65 7.

Rollinson, W. (1967). *A History of Man in the Lake District*. J. M. Dent & Sons Ltd, London. 162pp.

The Lake District Still Waters Partnership

Centre for Ecology and Hydrology

The Centre for Ecology and Hydrology (CEH) is one of the Centres and Surveys of the Natural Environment Research Council (NERC), and is the leading UK body for research, survey, and monitoring in terrestrial and freshwater environments. The Centre has nearly 500 scientific staff, and well-equipped laboratories and field facilities at nine sites throughout the United Kingdom.

Contact Address:

CEH Windermere, The Ferry House, Far Sawrey, Ambleside, Cumbria LA22 0LP, UK.

Tel: +44 (0)15394 42468. For further information:
http://www.ceh.ac.uk/

English Nature

English Nature promotes the conservation of England's wildlife and natural features. We were set up by the Environmental Protection Act 1990 and we are a statutory body funded by the Department of Environment, Food and Rural Affairs. We are responsible for undertaking and promoting nature conservation in England and we do this by advising Ministers and others on policies and activities affecting nature conservation in England; establishing and managing National Nature Reserves; advising the UK Government on the designation and management of sites under international conservation conventions and EC Directives; selecting and contributing towards the sustainable management of SSSIs, in partnership with landowners, occupiers and relevant statutory bodies; promoting conservation of the English countryside and its wildlife through initiatives such as the Species Recovery Programme and Biodiversity Action Plans.

Contact Address (Cumbria Team) :

Juniper House, Murley Moss, Oxenholme Road, Kendal, Cumbria LA9 7RL, UK.

Tel: +44 (0)1539 792800. For further information:
http://www.english-nature.org.uk/aboutlink.htm

Environment Agency

The Environment Agency is a non-departmental public body established by the Environment Act 1995. The Agency is the leading public organisation for protecting and improving the environment in England and Wales. This involves regulating industry, maintaining flood defences and water resources, monitoring the state of the environment and improving wildlife habitats. It is the Agency's policy to work in partnership with others and to make environmental information widely available.

Contact Address (North West Region, North Area):

The Environment Agency, Ghyll Mount, Gillan Way, Penrith 40 Business Park, Penrith, Cumbria CA11 9BP, UK.

Tel: +44 (0)1768 866666. For further information:
http://www.environment-agency.gov.uk/

Freshwater Biological Association

The Association conducts research into all aspects of freshwater science and technology, provides a Membership organisation and independent scientific opinion. The FBA provides scientific continuity – it was founded in 1929 and has a long history of achievements in freshwater science. This includes the publication of more than 2000 papers in recognised scientific journals and a series of independent publications (including identification keys for freshwater taxa, analytical methods, etc.). The FBA possesses one of the finest freshwater libraries in the world and provides essential advisory services to its members. Many national and international awards and honours have been bestowed upon the Association and its senior staff in recognition of the quality and importance of their scientific achievements.

Contact Address:

Freshwater Biological Association, The Ferry House, Far Sawrey, Ambleside, Cumbria LA22 0LP, UK.

Tel: +44 (0)15394 42468. For further information:
http://www.fba.org.uk/index.html

Lake District National Park Authority

The Lake District National Park Authority was established by Parliament in 1951 to protect the area's outstanding beauty and promote its quiet enjoyment by the public. As a local authority we also take into account the needs of the 40,000 or so people who live inside the National Park boundary.

The Lake District National Park Authority is a local government body which has two purposes: to conserve and enhance the natural beauty, wildlife and cultural heritage of the National Park, and to promote opportunities for the understanding and enjoyment of the special qualities of the National Park by the public. In pursuing these opportunities we will also seek to foster the economic and social well-being of local communities within the National Park.

Contact Address:

The Lake District National Park Authority, Murley Moss, Oxenholme Road, Kendal, Cumbria LA9 7RL, UK.

Tel: +44 (0)1539 724555. For further information:
   http://www.lake-district.gov.uk/authority/whowhat.htm

National Trust

The National Trust was founded in 1895 by three Victorian philanthropists: Miss Octavia Hill, Sir Robert Hunter and Canon Hardwicke Rawnsley. Concerned about the impact of uncontrolled development and industrialisation, they set up the Trust to act as a guardian for the nation in the acquisition and protection of threatened coastline, countryside and buildings.

Contact Address (North West (Cumbria & Lancashire)):

National Trust, The Hollens, Grasmere, Ambleside, Cumbria LA22 9QZ, UK.

Tel: +44 (0)15394 35599. For further information:
   http://www.nationaltrust.org.uk/main/

United Utilities

"...the challenge is to demonstrate how effective corporate responsibility can be integrated into everyday management..."!

Contact Address:

United Utilities, Dawson House, Great Sankey, Warrington WA5 3LW, UK.

Telephone: (+44) 1925 234000

For further information:
   http://www.unitedutilities.co.uk/